FISHERIES BIOLOGY

A Study in Population Dynamics

D. H. Cushing

Fisheries Biology

A Study in
Population Dynamics

THE UNIVERSITY OF WISCONSIN PRESS, 1968

Madison, Milwaukee, and London

Published by

The University of Wisconsin Press

Box 1379, Madison, Wisconsin 53701

The University of Wisconsin Press, Ltd.

27–29 Whitfield Street, London, W.1

Printed in the United States of America by

George Banta Company, Inc., Menasha, Wisconsin

Library of Congress Catalog Card Number 68–14033

Preface

In the spring of 1963, Professor A. D. Hasler asked me to give a series of lectures on fisheries biology to his graduate students in the Department of Zoology of the University of Wisconsin at Madison. The present text has been developed from those lectures, and is offered as a basis on which to build management and conservation principles for commercial fisheries.

Material is taken from the literature published on the results of fisheries research, some freshwater, but mainly marine, throughout the world. Because I live on the east coast of England, the literature I have used principally concerns research and problems dealing with the fisheries of northern Europe. Much of the important scientific literature is buried in the papers of more or less inaccessible journals. The basic concepts are those of E. S. Russell and Michael Graham, both former directors of the Fisheries Laboratory, Lowestoft, and of W. E. Ricker of the Fisheries Research Board of Canada. These ideas were put in analytic form by R. J. H. Beverton and S. J. Holt in their book *On the Dynamics of Exploited Fish Populations* (1957); in addition, their analyses made full use of growth and mortality data in yearly increments.

The book is addressed to students and teachers at the university level and to fisheries biologists, as well as to those administrators to whom a knowledge of fisheries biology is vital in order that they may practice sound conservation measures for the harvesting of fish on an international basis.

Fish taxonomists are few and overworked, and up-to-date scientific names covering the scope of the present volume are unavailable in any one publication. Where pertinent geographically, the nomenclature I have used follows that found in *Plymouth Marine Fauna* (Marine Biological Ass. of the United Kingdom, Plymouth; 2nd ed., 1931; 371 p.), *A List of Common and Scientific Names of the Better Known Fishes of the United States and Canada* (Amer. Fish. Soc., Washington, D.C.; Spec. Pub. No. 1, 2nd ed., 1960; 102 p.), G. V. Nikolsky, *Special Ichthyology* (published for the National Science Foundation and the Smithsonian Institution by the Israel Program for Scientific Translations, Jerusalem, 1961; 538 p.), and *Bulletin Statistique des Pêches Maritimes Cons. Perm. Intern. Explor. Mer*, 49 (1966), p. 72–80. The notations used are based on those of Beverton and Holt, as well as those in "A Standard Terminology and Notation for Fishery Dynamics," by S. J. Holt, J. A. Gulland, C. Taylor, and S. Kurita (1959, *J. Cons. Intern. Explor. Mer*, 24:239–42), accepted by the International Council for the Exploration of the Sea in Bergen, 1957.

I am grateful to my colleagues J. A. Gulland, F. R. Harden Jones, and A. C. Burd for reading the manuscript during the spring of 1964, and to Harold Jenner for the drafting work that most of the figures required. I am also grateful to H. A. Cole, Director of the Fisheries Laboratory at Lowestoft, not only for reading the text, but for allowing me to travel to Madison. To Professor Hasler I am indebted for having invited me there. The trip was made possible by a training grant from the United States Public Health Service.

D.H.C.

Lowestoft, Suffolk
September 1967

Contents

Illustrations

FISHERIES BIOLOGY
A Study in Population Dynamics

1 | The Scope of Fisheries Biology

In the last ten years, the world's catch of fish (about 50 million tons in 1965) in freshwater and in the sea has doubled. Some stocks, such as the sardine-like fishes off African coasts, are underexploited. Others, like the bottom-living fish stocks in the northeastern and northwestern Atlantic, are exploited at about the right rate. Other stocks are overfished. For example, Antarctic blue whales have been fished nearly to extinction. It is unlikely that they will recover for many, many years. So an annual production of more than 1 million tons has been lost. This book describes methods used in the study of fisheries biology by which stocks may be measured, conserved, and properly exploited.

In the open sea, stocks of fish are the common property of all nations, but fishermen have found that the more heavily they fished, the more their catches have declined. As a consequence, most countries have set up governmental laboratories where scientists have been able to study the biology of the fish stocks, their population dynamics, and the means of sharing them internationally. Very large quantities of information have been collected, and some fish stocks are now the most fully studied of all wild animal populations.

There are two branches of fisheries biology. One is the study of the natural history of the stocks, and is concerned with how the fish spawn, grow, and feed. Its primary purpose is to delimit the stocks or the unit populations. The other branch is the study of the dynamics of such populations—the rates at which fish grow, die, and reproduce. Most fisheries biology consists of the description of individual fisheries in terms of the fish stocks and of the dynamics of those stocks. The natural history is that needed to support the dynamic studies of the population.

3

Fish Population Studies

In a very simple form of population dynamics (Fig. 1), the presence of senile fish is indicative of very little fishing pressure. The figure represents two *Tilapia* (*Tilapia esculenta* Graham) caught in the Victoria Nyanza in East Africa by Michael Graham (Graham, 1958). The top one is a fish of moderate age in good condition; the bottom one appears to be a senile animal, with its heavy jaw and gill cover and its large pectoral fin. The first was taken from a well-fished population in the Kavirondo Gulf of the Victoria Nyanza, and the second from a very lightly fished population in the Emin Pasha Gulf of the Victoria Nyanza. Most of the fish in the catch in the Emin Pasha Gulf were old ones. There were very few old ones in the much larger catches from the Kavirondo Gulf. Moderate or heavy fishing increased the chance of death, and eliminated most of the senile fish.

Market statistics.—A fair fraction of the fish population is counted and weighed on the fish quays and markets. A complex system has been developed to sample the catch on the quay and the stock in the sea. From each ship, details of catch, position, and number of fishing hours are recorded on the fish quays. The time spent fishing is called the fishing effort. The catch per unit of fishing effort (i.e., cwt/100 hr trawling, number of tuna per 100 hooks, etc.) is a proper index of stock (Ricker, 1940; Beverton and Holt, 1957). Consequently, charts can be made of catch per effort (or stock density) of different species on different grounds month by month. British catches of many species come from the North Sea, Faeroe Islands, Iceland, Barents Sea, and East Greenland, and in recent years British fishermen have returned to the Grand Banks off Newfoundland.

Not only are records made of catch, position, and time spent fishing, but fish are also measured for length at the market. With its nose rammed against the stub of a board, each fish is smoothed down to the tail, and measured to the end of the spread tail fin. The measurers take a fish box, the weight of which is known, and count and record the lengths of the fish in it. Hence, a very complete picture of the length-frequency distribution of the catch is constructed for each area, each day, each week, or each month. It is quite simple to express such distributions in catch per unit of effort or stock density (e.g., no. cwt of 60-cm cod [*Gadus morhua* Linnaeus] per 100 hr fishing from Bear Island, between Norway and Spitsbergen, in June). In 1961, 750,000 fish of various species were measured in this way in English ports (Great Britain. . . . 1962. Fish stock record, 1961). Good estimates are thus available of the length distribution of the catch and also of catch per unit of effort—and hence, the stock.

Figure 1. An elementary form of population analysis. The top picture is of a middle-aged *Tilapia* caught from a moderately fished stock in the Victoria Nyanza. The lower picture is of a senile fish from a relatively unfished stock. Senile fish are easily recognizable and readily caught; they are not found readily in a moderately fished stock. The presence of senile fish thus indicates absence of fishing. From Graham, 1958.

Growth rates and death rates.—Because the ages of fish can be readily measured, it is possible to estimate the growth rates and death rates of fish populations. Otoliths are collected from most fish, but scales are taken from herring (*Clupea harengus* Linnaeus) and salmon (*Oncorhynchus* sp. and *Salmo* sp.). Figure 2 shows an otolith from a plaice (*Pleuronectes platessa* Linnaeus) and a scale from a herring. The age of each fish is readily determined from the annual rings found on both otolith (Hickling, 1931; Rollefsen, 1934) and scale (Dahl, 1907; Lea, 1929).

Age-and-length correlation tables are constructed from rather small samples of scales and otoliths; the tables are then used to convert the

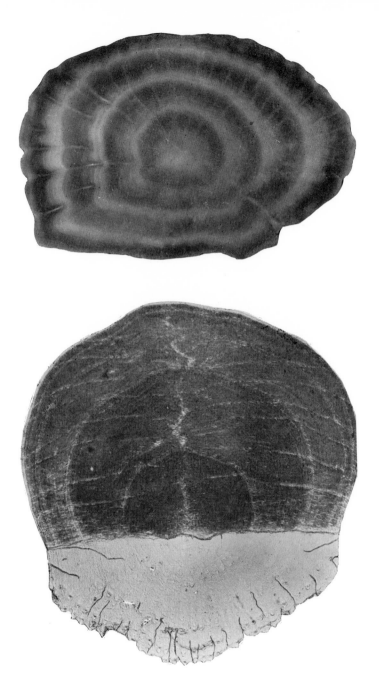

Figure 2. An otolith from a plaice (*top*) and a scale from a herring (*bottom*). The rings on both are annual rings, so the ages of both species can be readily determined.

large numbers of length measurements into estimates of age (Fridriksson, 1934). For example, 400 fish a week are aged in the East Anglian herring fishery (off the east coast of England), but up to 10,000 fish a week may be measured in length. Thus, we are able to express both the catch and the stock in terms of age, e.g., as so many cwt of four-year-old fish caught or as per 100 hr fishing in the stock. Because fish can be easily aged and this information can be carried right through the sampling system, the ages of fish populations are very much better known than those of other wild species. Lengths for an age class, based on the catches, can be compared from year to year to yield growth rates. Within a fully recruited year class (i.e., a brood of fish born in a given year), the decline in stock density from year to year is due to mortality; the ratio of stock densities can thus be used to estimate mortality. Figure 3 (*left*) shows the increase in weight for various ages of plaice based on market measurements, and Figure 3 (*right*) shows the average mortality of plaice for a period of ten years, based on estimates of stock density. Both estimates are averaged from a large quantity of information collected from the market, and they are the bones of fisheries research.

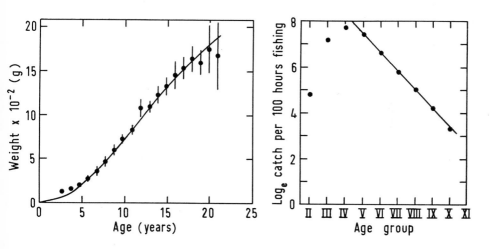

Figure 3. Left. The growth in weight of the plaice in years of life. The estimates are taken from market measurements and are averaged for the period 1929–38.

Right. The mortality of plaice between the ages of five and ten years. The estimates are taken from the system of market measurements and statistics of catch per unit of effort. They were averaged for the period 1929–38. Both figures adapted from Beverton and Holt, 1957.

Independent estimates of stock.—Because estimates of stock density can become biased (see Chapter 4), independent measures of the stock in the sea are needed. Most commercially fished species, except herring, lay eggs that float in midwater. Such eggs can be readily caught by silk or nylon plankton nets and counted, as in the case of pilchard eggs (*Sardina pilchardus* [Walbaum]) in the English Channel (Fig. 4). Five cruises were made in April, May, June, July, and August 1950, extending over the entire Channel (Cushing, 1957). The area was split into statistical rectangles, with a number of stations in each rectangle. The number of eggs produced at a point in time (e.g., the midpoint of a cruise) is given as

$$\sum (OAQ) ,$$

where O is the average number of eggs caught beneath one square
          meter in an early developmental stage in one rectangle,
       A is the area of that rectangle in m², and
       Q is the temperature coefficient of egg development.
Each point on the curve represents the sum for the whole Channel (Fig. 4); the whole curve represents the total production of stage I eggs (hatched eggs before the appearance of the neural crest) through a rather extensive spawning period. The egg takes 40–72 hours to hatch in the Channel, depending on the temperature. Because it is a rather short period, errors in temperature conversion are likely to be small ones. The standard deviation is

$$\overline{Q}\sqrt{\sum\left(O^2A^2\frac{s^2}{k}\right)}$$

where s^2 is the variance of the estimate of numbers in each rectangle,
       k is the number of stations in the rectangle, and
       $\overline{Q}$ is the average temperature coefficient for the whole cruise;
          errors in temperature determination and in the estimate of
          the temperature coefficient have been ignored.
   The number of adult pilchards in the English Channel is given by the number of eggs produced (Fig. 4), divided by twice the number of eggs per female; the number is $10^{10} \times 2.2 \times 0.45$. The error, or sampling variation, is a multiplicative one because the distribution is a log normal one (where the logarithms of a set of variate-value are distributed according to a normal curve). English (1964) has pointed out that the error between cruises is high and that the cost in cash of reducing it to manageable proportions may even be prohibitive. However, in principle, this estimate of population numbers can be used as

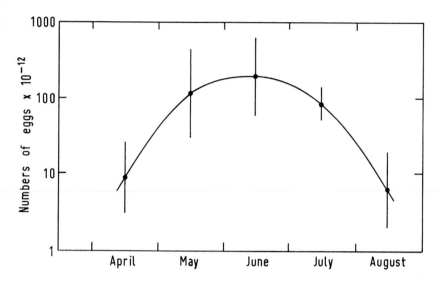

Figure 4. The production of pilchard eggs in the English Channel. The vertical lines indicate the error on each estimate of production. Adapted from Cushing, 1957.

a check against the stock-density estimates made with catches per unit effort.

The theory of fisheries dynamics.—The fourth characteristic of fisheries dynamics is common to all population dynamics; it is the mathematical theory. As in many branches of science today, it involves the making of models. Model-making is a form of conceptual experiment and is probably the only way of unraveling complex situations where many things happen at once. The theory has been developed by Baranov (1918), Beverton and Holt (1957), and Ricker (1958); the latter author summarizes and refers to a number of his own papers published between 1940 and 1958. But the simplest formulation of the theory of fishing is Russell's (1931). His equation is

$$P_2 = P_1 + G + R + Z',\tag{1}$$

where P_2 is stock at time t_2,

P_1 is stock at time t_1,

G is growth between t_1 and t_2,

R is recruitment between t_1 and t_2, and

Z' is mortality between t_1 and t_2.

If the stock is to remain in a steady state, the gains from growth and recruitment must be balanced by losses due to mortality.

A more complex derivation of this equation appears in Chapter 4, where stock is expressed in terms of numbers or weight, and where the mathematics and notation of Beverton and Holt (1957) are used. These authors use the description of growth and mortality with reference to age as an essential part of the central equations in an analytic manner. This is the major advance that they have made beyond those of the other theoreticians.

Above, then, are the four branches of population dynamics used in fisheries research. The first is the sampling of the catch on the quay and of the stock in the sea. The second is the conversion of length measurements made at the market into estimates of age in units of stock density. The third branch is the creation of independent measures of stock density. The fourth is the development of models in mathematical terms.

The Biology of the Stocks

The powerful theoretical weapons developed for analyzing the changes in fish populations are of little use if the populations cannot be delimited. Sometimes the population is isolated (like Faeroe cod) and the methods can be used directly. Where populations mix, extensive biological analysis is required to delimit them. Three types of biological work are needed for this purpose: the study of migration; the study of the unit stock in itself; and the study of growth and recruitment—where characteristics often differ between stocks or subpopulations.

Migration.—The study of migration is fundamental to fisheries research. The fish appear to make use of the current structures for purposes of spawning, feeding, and the positions of their nurseries (Meek, 1916). Eggs and larvae drift away from spawning ground to nursery ground; the adults migrate back to the spawning ground. This ensures that the larvae drift to a nursery ground close to the feeding ground.

For example, albacore (*Thunnus alalunga* Bonnaterre) that have been tagged off the California coast migrate to fishing grounds close to Japan (Otsu, 1960). Most journeys last about a year, but some are less. On a straight course, this would be fast—but when the trip is made by traveling at random around the North Pacific gyre, it becomes a very fast migration. It is possible that the albacore live constantly in the gyre, as indicated by the monthly progress of catches along the Kuroshio and eastward into the Kuroshio extension. Thus, this particular stock might be considered as a body of fish living in the North Pacific gyre.

Similarly, the Norwegian herring drift in a circuit around the Norwegian Sea. As the stock spawning along the Norwegian coast near Bergen comprises the same fish that visit Jan Mayen and Iceland in the summer, the group ranging within a unit of water circulation might possibly be unified into a single stock.

Growth and feeding.—The biology of the North Sea herring is considerably influenced by the quality of the food, for their growth changes have been associated with changes in the quantity of the copepod *Calanus finmarchicus* Gunnerus in the sea (see Chapter 7). It is possible that a whole complex of fisheries originated from changes of growth, which in turn causes changes in recruitment.

Hardy et al. (1936) started much of this work when they gave small plankton nets to the driftermen and taught them to recognize *Calanus*. The nets, torpedo-like in shape and operation, were towed astern of the ship. In one summer at least, high catches of herring were associated with high catches of *Calanus* (Fig. 5). Because they aggregate at patches of *Calanus*, the herring grow more quickly, particularly if the food patches are extensive. Since the growth of fish is directly modifiable by such environmental changes, this field of study is important from the point of view of population change. It is often assumed that a population is modified in quantity only at recruitment. The changes in herring growth in the last decade in the North Sea account for an increase in weight of stock of nearly 20 percent.

Spawning.—Two groups of spawning grounds are used by the southern North Sea herring (Fig. 6): (a) Sandettié and Cap Blanc Nez; (b) Ailly and the Creux St. Nicolas. Each is small, perhaps 2–3 km long by 500 m wide. Each year the fish spawn in the same places. The exact positions were discovered by trawlers using echo sounders; very dense areas of echo traces were found only there and on two assembly grounds, Hinder and Vergoyer. Trawlers have not worked elsewhere between 1950 and 1962, except on one occasion in 1951 when they found a patch of spawning herring southeast of Beachy Head. The timing of spawning is very regular. The fish appear near the Sandettié Light Vessel during the first ten days of November (Ancellin and Nédelèc, 1959). On these grounds in November and December 1962, 150 large vessels were working by day and perhaps 100 smaller pair trawlers by both day and night.

Fisheries biology must ultimately depend on the proper answer to the biological problems here: (a) to understand the spawning mech-

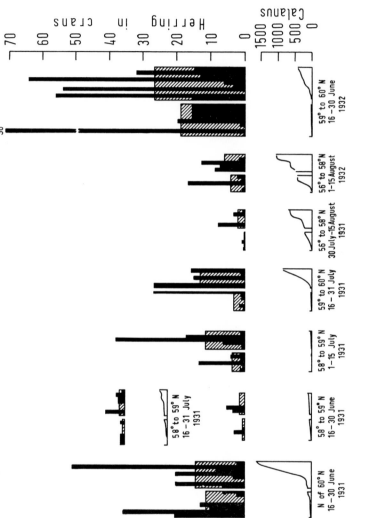

Figure 5. An association of high herring catches with high densities of *Calanus*, the preferred food of the herring. The catches in crans for dense and thin aggregations of *Calanus* are shown as histograms, and the diagonal hatching indicates the average catches. The density of *Calanus*, estimated on the same night as the catch, is shown below the histograms as a thin line split at the median to separate "rich" and "poor" concentrations of *Calanus*. Adapted from Hardy et al., 1936.

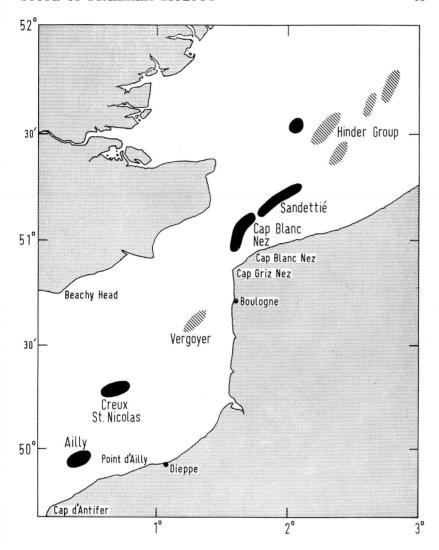

Figure 6. The spawning grounds of the herring in the southern North Sea. Black areas indicate spawning grounds; diagonally hatched areas are assembly grounds. Adapted from Ancellin and Nédelèc, 1959.

anisms and how the fish remain within the very narrow spawning grounds; (b) to understand how the herring can appear on the spawning grounds so regularly, when their cruising speeds are less than the maximum speeds of the tidal streams. If the fish spawn regularly on the same restricted grounds, they may belong to the same spawning group, and such evidence can be used to establish the unity of a fish stock or subpopulation.

The Biology of a Fishery

Because fisheries biology is a combination of population dynamics and natural history, any fishery should be describable in terms of the biology of the stock and of its dynamics. This theme is illustrated by the Downs herring of the Southern Bight of the North Sea and the course of the fisheries there in autumn and winter (Fig. 7). The Downs herring comprise a population of North Sea herring, the characteristics of which are noted below. South of 53°30′ N there is one group of herring that spawns on the grounds just described. North of this line, around the edges of the Dogger Bank, there are trawl fisheries on spawning herring from mid-September to mid-October. These exploit another stock—the Dogger stock, as opposed to the Downs stock which spawns in the Straits of Dover and in the eastern English Channel. The first fisheries for Downs herring are drift-net operations in five areas during October and November: (1) north of the Norfolk Banks, north of Lowestoft; (2) near Smith's Knoll Light Vessel, northeast of Lowestoft; (3) on the Brown Ridges, east of Lowestoft; (4) on the Schouwen ground, east-southeast of Lowestoft; and (5) on the Galloper ground, south-southeast of Lowestoft. These small subfisheries operate roughly in the order given as the herring move south. In November and December, trawl fisheries are found on the spawning grounds at Sandettié and Ailly. Then from December until March, pair trawlers work close to the French, Dutch, and Belgian coasts on the spent herring (spawned) drifting north along the continental coast. The fisheries thus move south as the herring move south, and north as the spent fish move north, and the movement of the fish is best interpreted as a

Figure 7 (facing). The progression of herring fisheries in the Southern Bight of the North Sea. The vertically hatched areas represent the spawning fisheries around the Dogger Bank in September and October. The diamond hatching shows the positions of the drift-net fisheries in the Southern Bight in October and November. The black arrows pointing southward represent the southerly movement of the fish through the fisheries. The black patches indicate the trawl fisheries on the spawning grounds in November and December. The long black arrow along the continental coast represents the course of the pair-trawler fishery working for spent herring in December, January, and February (and in some years, later). The dashed arrow represents the course of the old Lowestoft spring drift-net fishery which lasted from February to April. Fathom depths are indicated by the finer lines of dots and dashes.

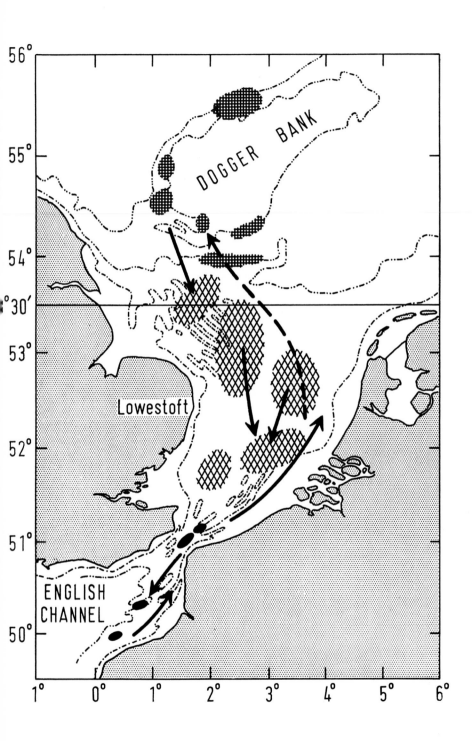

migration. There is some evidence from tagging experiments to support this theory (Bolster, 1955). The old Lowestoft spring herring fishery, which died out in the 1930's, was an essential link in the chain of migration. It started off the Dutch coast and moved from there to the Brown Ridges, the Norfolk Banks, and to the Silver Pit (just south of the Dogger Bank), between February and April.

The biological data in the East Anglian fishery can be summarized in two diagrams. Figure 8 shows the age sequence in stock density by weeks in the East Anglian fishery for 1935 (Hodgson, 1957). The young fish, those three and four years old, first enter the fishery in October; the older fish, those seven and eight years old, come in November. Because the younger fish come earlier and the older ones later, the age-sampling, in order to be adequate, has to be completed in short time intervals of three days or a week. Figure 9 shows the total age distributions in numbers per drifter shot (or stock density) from 1935 to 1960. The same sort of picture is found in the samples from the trawl fishery based on Boulogne and in those from the spent herring fishery based on Ostend. There are two notable biological features—a change in the recruitment pattern in 1950–52, and the gradual loss of the older fish in the late 1950's, due to increasing mortality. Before 1950 the recruits came into the fishery at two time intervals, some at three years of age and others at four, a year later; by 1952, all recruits came in at three years of age and this situation has remained ever since. These events are described in Chapter 3, but they suffice here to demonstrate that the fishery is complex and that it must be interpreted in proper biological terms before its population dynamics can be adequately used.

Summary

There are two branches of fisheries biology. The first concerns the dynamics of the stocks, the estimates of catch and stock density on the markets, the aging of the fish in terms of stock density, the use of independent measures of abundance, and the use of mathematical models. The second branch involves the study of migration, growth, spawning, and recruitment in terms of the stock. A third part of fisheries biology describes fisheries in terms of the biology of the stock and its dynamics.

The detailed biology is extensive in range, requiring the basic physiology of metabolism (as applied to growth studies), of sensation (as applied to the study of migration), and of endocrines (as applied to reproduction). To understand the oceanic environment, considerable knowledge of the physics of the ocean is needed, for example, how water

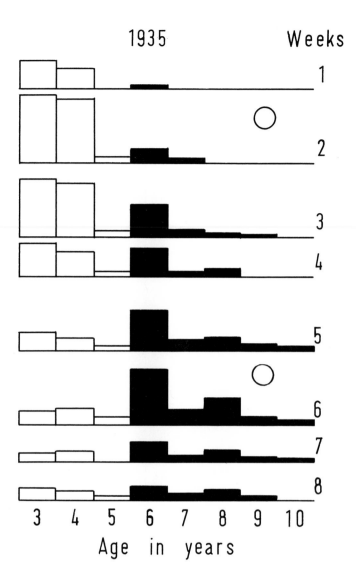

Figure 8. The age distributions (abscissa) in stock density (ordinate) in the East Anglian herring fishery for eight successive weeks in 1935, from early October (*top series*) to late November (*bottom series*). The three-, four-, and five-year-old fish (blank columns) entered the fishery in October. The six-, seven-, and eight-year-old fish (black columns) entered in November. The week of the full moon is shown by the open circles; the highest catches are made at or near the dates of the full moon. Adapted from Hodgson, 1957.

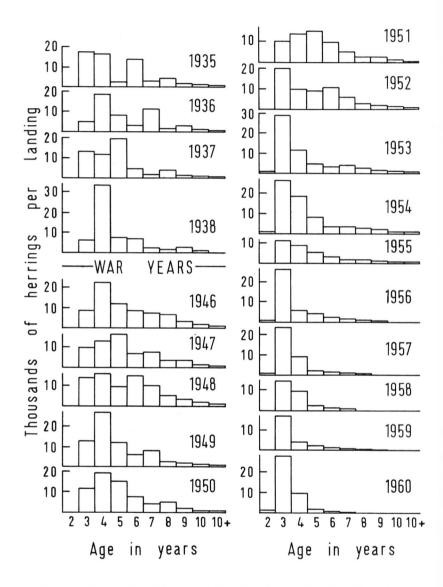

Figure 9. The age distributions of the East Anglian herring fishery in stock density from 1935 to 1960. Before 1952, the fish recruited partly at three years of age and partly at four; in 1952 and subsequently, recruitment was complete at three. Note the severe loss of older fish during the second half of the 1950's.

masses move and how light penetrates the sea. Particular instrumental skills are needed, such as a knowledge of acoustics and electronics. The extensive range is also exemplified in the results of dynamic studies. Very large quantities of data are available on distribution in time and space of fish species in terms of stock densities. Methods of handling the data are varied, and are used in association with tagging techniques and other forms of population estimates.

In this book, two chapters deal with the preliminary biology needed for any stock analysis, in the study of migration and the study of unit stocks or subpopulations. The next three chapters describe the measures of abundance on which all stock analysis is based, the use of fishing to separate the causes of mortality, and the means by which the best use can be made of stocks of fish. The effect of the environment on fish populations is examined in a chapter on growth, another deals with stock and recruitment, and still another with the oceanic boundaries where fish appear to gather. The final chapter, entitled "The Future of Fisheries Research," describes some areas of interest which might develop into valuable lines of research.

2 | Migration

THE study of migration is fundamental to fisheries biology because the migration circuit delimits the area in which the stock or subpopulation lives. The eggs of most marine fishes are pelagic, and, like them, their larvae drift with the tides and the ocean currents. From the spawning grounds the larvae may drift for considerable distances toward the nursery grounds. Indeed, the smallest larvae (or leptocephali) of the eel drift for thousands of miles in the Atlantic (Schmidt, 1922).

The needs of larval and adolescent fish differ greatly from those of the adults. Immature fish usually live in shallower water and feed on smaller creatures than do the adults. An example of the extreme contrast between the different environment of adults and immatures is found in eel (*Anguilla* sp.) and salmon. Immature eels, after metamorphosis, live in freshwater, and adults spawn in the ocean, whereas immature salmon live in the ocean and the adults spawn in freshwater. Heincke's law (1913), as applied to plaice, provides another and simpler expression of the difference between the environments of immatures and adults: Larger plaice live in deeper water. Despite the contrast between the environments of juveniles and adults and despite the great distances over which the larvae and juveniles drift from spawning ground to nursery ground, the spawning grounds tend to be fixed. It is the migratory circuit between spawning ground and adult feeding ground that limits the range of stock. To understand migration, then, is to understand why there are geographical boundaries to the stock.

Adolescent fish often recruit to adult stocks on the adult feeding ground. For example, the immature arctic cod, a population of the

Atlantic cod living in the Barents Sea, have only to move from the top of the Svalbard shelf to join the adult stocks in the deeper water on the slope of the shelf. Likewise, the nursery grounds of the North Sea herring lie near the adult migration routes between spawning ground and feeding ground (Burd and Cushing, 1962).

Adults of both cod and herring migrate to a spawning ground from which the larvae and juveniles drift to the nursery ground, which supplies the adult stock with recruits in later years. Figure 10 shows the migration circuit in diagrammatic form. Because the adults swim from feeding ground to spawning ground, allowing the drifted larvae to recruit to the feeding ground, the range of migration is roughly the range of larval and juvenile drift. To reach their spawning grounds the adults swim against the current that carries the larvae, a contranatant migration. The word "contranatant" means that, to reach the spawning ground, adult fish must apparently move against those currents that drift the larvae away from it. Some form of movement against the current, directing the migration, is not included in the connotation. Not only are there possibly undescribed countercurrents, but migration by an oriented movement against a current requires that the fish refer their movements to external objects independently of the current. Such referents are sometimes hard to find.

Because of the drift of larvae and juveniles and the contranatant movement of the adults, the stock is contained within a constant circuit so long as the spawning ground is always in the same place. The arctic cod larvae drift away from the Vest Fjord in northern Norway,

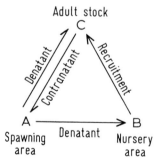

Figure 10. Diagrammatic migration circuit used by fish. Adults apparently migrate against currents from feeding ground to spawning ground, and the larvae drift to the nursery ground. From there the adolescent fish can recruit to the adult stock on the feeding ground. Courtesy of F. R. Harden Jones.

where they were hatched, riding the West Spitsbergen current and the North Cape current (Fig. 11) until they reach the Svalbard shelf and the banks of the southeastern Barents Sea where they settle (Corlett, 1958). The adolescent fish move off these banks into deeper water (Maslov, 1944) and join the adult stocks that live there in autumn just before the spawning migration starts. Then, contranatantly, the adults travel apparently against the West Spitsbergen current and the North Cape current until they reach the Vest Fjord and spawn (Trout, 1957). The seasonal use of the currents by the fish has been called the hydrographic containment of the stock. Larvae arise on a single spawning ground and, if this ground is always used, a coherence in stock is maintained from generation to generation. Then the stock is a unit population, or, as fisheries biologists say, a unit stock. Early fisheries biologists separated Faeroe cod from Iceland cod and from arctic cod as stocks merely because there were very deep waters between the Faeroes and Iceland and between the Faeroes and Norway, across which the cod would not swim. Recently, a cod has crossed the Atlantic (Gulland and Williamson, 1962), but the suppositions of the early fisheries biologists were right; separate stocks are involved and for the simple reason suggested.

Before the migrations of particular fish species are described, the cruising- and maximum-speed capacities of fish should be noted. Fish cruise at 3 fish lengths per sec and their fastest speed is about 10 fish lengths per sec (Blaxter and Dickson, 1959; Bainbridge, 1960). Thus, a 70-cm cod cruises at about 4.2 knots and a 25-cm herring at about 1.5 knots. In the southern North Sea, tidal streams move swiftly, up to 2.5 or 3 knots. A cod could cruise more quickly than this during the entire tidal cycle; a herring could cruise more quickly for part of it; a 12-cm sprat (*Clupea sprattus* Linnaeus) could never compete with the tidal streams except at slack water.

The Atlantic Eel

The study of the eel's migration was the first piece of work undertaken by Schmidt (1914, 1915) as the Danish part in international investigations of the North Sea during the first years of this century. Schmidt examined the vertebral counts from samples throughout Europe and found that their means were all the same (Schmidt, 1914, 1922). His conclusion was that a single stock supplied eels to all European rivers. Therefore, when the ripening eels go down to the sea, they must spawn out in the ocean, at some distance from the long European coastline. Accordingly, Schmidt made larval surveys outward into the Atlantic and charted the spawning grounds as the places

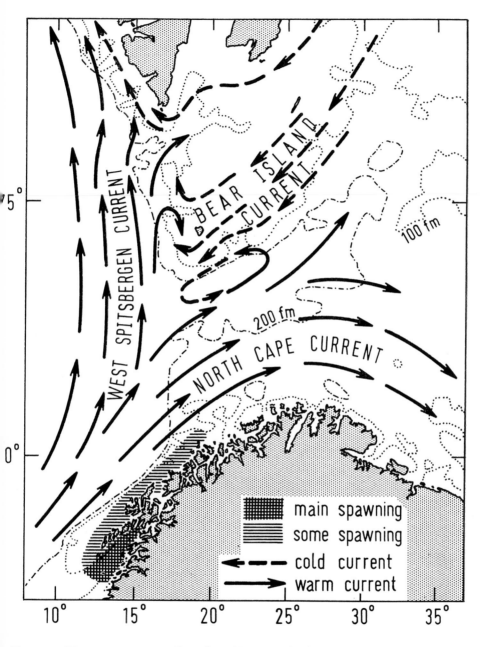

Figure 11. The current system off northern Norway. The arctic cod larvae ride the West Spitsbergen current and the North Cape current until they reach the Svalbard shelf or the southeastern Barents Sea. Adapted from Corlett, 1958.

where the smallest leptocephali were caught (Fig. 12). Unexpectedly, he found that the American eel (*Anguilla rostrata* [LeSueur]) also spawned in roughly the same area of the Sargasso Sea as the European eel (*Anguilla anguilla* Linnaeus). The spawning ground of the American eel lies some distance west of that of the European eel (Fig. 12). The two species are distinguished only by a difference of seven vertebrae in their vertebral counts. Distributions of vertebral counts (Fig. 13) —a mean of 114.7 ± 1.3 for *A. anguilla* and one of 107.2 ± 1.3 for *A. rostrata*—indicate very little overlap between the two species (cour-

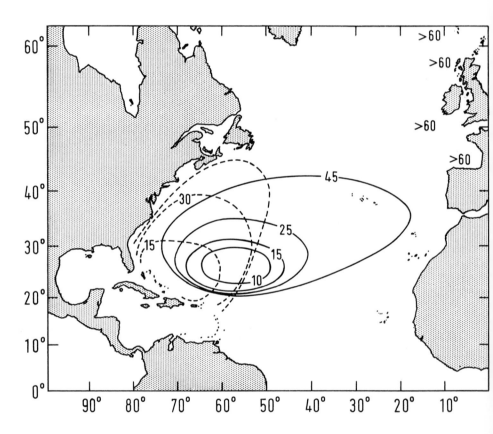

Figure 12. The distribution of larval eels, the leptocephali, in the North Atlantic. The solid line represents the distribution of the leptocephali of *Anguilla anguilla*, the dashed line that of the leptocephali of *A. rostrata*. The contours represent areas within which larvae less than 10 mm in length, for example, were found. The patches of smallest larvae occurred in the Sargasso Sea. Adapted from Schmidt, 1922.

tesy of F. R. Harden Jones, from data tabulated in Ege, 1939). This
is virtually the same figure as that published by Schmidt (1914), but
Ege had a greater number of observations on the American eel. This
difference in number of vertebrae is a large one, much greater than can
be generated merely by environmental effects. Schmidt (1917) made
extensive studies of the effects of temperature differences on the vertebral counts of *Zoarces*, a genus of the blenny family. From this work
he was able to distinguish environmental and genetic effects, and accordingly to imply that the big difference in vertebral count found
between the two eel species was a genetic one.

The American eel grows quickly and metamorphoses after a year,
whereas the European eel grows slowly and metamorphoses after two
and one-half years (Ehrenbaum and Marukawa, 1913; Fig. 14). The
young European eel drifts at the surface and appears to eat diatoms
and coccolithophorids. Inasmuch as the drift of water across the
Atlantic takes about two and one-half years (Iselin, 1936) and the

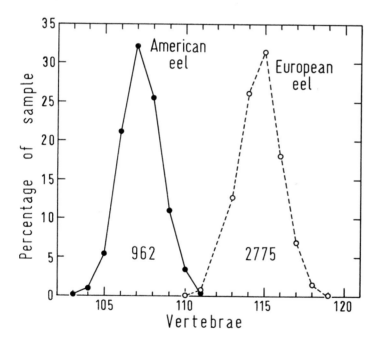

Figure 13. The distributions in vertebral sum for the European
eel (*Anguilla anguilla*) and the American eel (*A. rostrata*). Courtesy
of F. R. Harden Jones, from data tabulated in Ege, 1939.

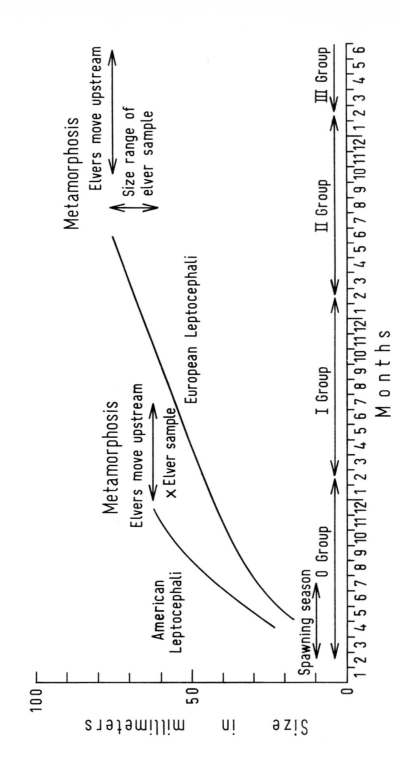

Figure 14. The growth rates of the American and European eels. Courtesy of F. R. Harden Jones.

leptocephali seem to remain within this drift, there is a correlation with the probable ages of the young eels; thus, the slow growth to metamorphosis of the European eel is apparently associated with the time needed to cross the ocean. The faster-growing American eel does not have so far to go and the leptocephali metamorphose within the year. It is worth contrasting the growth of the European eel to a few g in three years with that of some tuna species (e.g., Bluefin, *Thunnus thynnus* [Linnaeus]), which in the same time grow to well over 50 kg (Tiews, 1963). After metamorphosis, the eels move up the rivers where they may live for many years. Toward the end of this phase of their lives, the adults turn from yellow to silver, their gonads ripen, and the gut shrivels (Grassi, 1896), the eye enlarges and the retinal pigment turns to deep-sea gold (Carlisle and Denton, 1959). Then the fish are ready to put to sea. Presumably they swim to the Sargasso, to spawn there and die.

The adult migration is, or rather, must be, of the same magnitude as the larval drift. The larval drift is slow, and growth of the leptocephali is astonishingly slow during their very specialized existence. The stocks of both eel species are contained oceanographically within the North Atlantic gyre; leptocephali of both the American and European species ride the current systems to the coasts of the two respective continents. It is not known how they segregate, or how the adults return to the Sargasso Sea. They might drift south with the Canaries current and then west with the North Atlantic gyre, or they might move in the slow countercurrent under the Gulf Stream (Swallow and Worthington, 1961).

Schmidt's presumption of a single European stock was probably right, justified by its containment in the North Atlantic gyre. It was not, however, a necessary conclusion from the consistency of the mean vertebral counts of eels from most of the European rivers. The combination of single spawning ground at the root of the North Atlantic circulation system and homogeneous vertebral counts provides good evidence of there being a single stock.

The Pacific Salmon

Fish of the Pacific salmon group spawn on the gravel redds in rivers during the autumn and winter. Their larvae take sixty days to hatch (Gilbert, 1914), and the young fish spend a year or so in lakes and rivers before swimming down to the sea. Smolts of the Atlantic salmon (*Salmo salar* Linnaeus) may move out to sea at two years of age (J. W. Jones, 1959), and in some Norwegian rivers smolts do not come down to the sea until they are six years old (J. W. Jones, 1959).

The Pacific salmon are fished by the Japanese south of the Aleutian Islands, over a thousand miles from land. Sockeye (*Oncorhynchus nerka* [Walbaum]), chum (*O. keta* [Walbaum]), pink (*O. gorbuscha* [Walbaum]), and coho salmon (*O. kisutch* [Walbaum]) are caught in this area from the open Pacific by drift nets 50–80 km long (Fukuhara, 1955).

The salmon are located by means of echo traces on an echo sounder. The hyperbolic trace is caused by a target crossing the rather wide sound beam; it is first picked up at extreme range, and then, as it crosses the beam, the range shortens as it reaches the point nearest the ship; it then opens again. On the recorder, these changes in range appear in time as the hyperbolic trace, time moving from left to right on the record. The vertical extent of the trace on the paper is the same as the transmitted pulse length. The pulse length is the distance in range in which the transmitted pulse of sound endures—about three or four feet. Because the pulse received in the hyperbolic trace is the same length all through the record, the target is a single fish. A shoal yields a compound trace, the received pulse length of which varies in time.

The notable feature about salmon migration is that the fish appear to return to spawn in the stream in which they were born. This parent-stream hypothesis is supported by a large quantity of evidence, two examples of which are illustrated here—one from work done at Cultus Lake in British Columbia and the other from McClinton Creek in British Columbia. Cultus Lake, where the sockeye spawn and eventually return (Table 1), drains into the Fraser River. Of 1,000 downstream migrants that were fin-clipped as smolts on their way to the sea, 900 were lost at sea. Recoveries were obtained for 100: of these, 75 were returning salmon caught by fishing boats off the mouth of the Fraser River (at the time of these experiments there was no Japanese oceanic fishing), and 25 returned to Cultus Lake where they were re-

Table 1.—The return of salmon to Cultus Lake

Season	Year			
	1929	1930	1931	1932
Winter	Hatched	In lake	At sea	At sea
Spring	In lake	To sea	At sea	At sea
Summer	In lake	At sea	At sea	At sea
Autumn	In lake	At sea	At sea	Return to spawn

captured (Harden Jones, in press, after Foerster, 1936). No marked fish were retaken elsewhere than from Cultus Lake and it is this fact that supports the parent-stream hypothesis.

Table 2 summarizes some work done on the pink salmon in McClinton Creek (Pritchard, 1938, 1939). In 1934, 2,941 marked fish returned to the creek; 324 were caught in the fishery at Massett Inlet on the way upstream. Of 11 marked fish recovered elsewhere, 7 were taken far from McClinton Creek. These 7 constitute a very small proportion indeed, and Pritchard (1948) shows that such straying to other streams is very much less than might be expected from a random search of other rivers by the fish. These facts also support the parent-stream hypothesis. Another conclusion from the data is that the vast majority of salmon are lost at sea, presumably eaten, or perhaps caught.

This brief survey indicates, then, that the adult salmon migration is probably of the same range as the larval and juvenile drift; this hypothesis assumes that the smolts drift down the Fraser River and around the Alaskan gyre. The adult fish segregate to their parent stream and the stock is that body of fish entering the stream as adults or as smolts leaving it. If the salmon from different streams live together at sea, the oceanic fishing mortality will be generated randomly with respect to the different rivers; and if this loss were the largest component of fishing mortality, it might be practical to treat the salmon from the Pacific coast of North America as a single stock. But such a concept might become dramatically difficult to apply to separate groups like those

Table 2.—The return of salmon to McClinton Creek

MOVEMENT PATTERN

Year 1	Autumn	Autumnal spawning run
Year 2	Spring	Spring migration of fry to the sea
	Autumn	No autumnal spawning run
Year 3	Spring	No spring migration of fry to the sea
	Autumn	Autumnal spawning run of spring downstream migrants of year 2

MARKING AND RECAPTURE DATA

	Spring downstream migrants			Autumnal adult return	
Year	No. unmarked	No. marked	Year	No. unmarked	No. marked
1931	5,200,000	185,057	1932	15,504 (0.30%)	96 (0.05%)
1933	2,150,000	107,949	1934	152,255 (7.08%)	2,941 (2.72%)
1935	12,500,000	85,634	1936	52,277 (0.42%)	35 (0.04%)

from Cultus Lake or McClinton Creek, in which mortality would vary capriciously.

North Sea Plaice

In the southern North Sea, there appear to be three spawning groups of plaice—in the German Bight, in the Southern Bight, and in the Flamborough Head area (Fig. 15; Simpson, 1959). This simple figure summarizes a very large quantity of material collected at sea since 1911. In the Southern Bight, the spawning season lasts from December to March, peaking in January; in the Flamborough Head area, it lasts from January to March, peaking in March; in the German Bight, it lasts from January to April, peaking in February. The spawning seasons between the three areas differ by about a month. From the Southern Bight, currents carry the larvae to the continental coast; after five weeks, they settle to the bottom and metamorphose, living almost among the breakers (Simpson, 1959). As juvenile fish, they spread outward from the coast, and in three years reach a depth of 20 m and a size that ranges in length from 10 cm to 23 cm (Heincke, 1913). It is likely that the recruit fish join the Southern Bight spawning group of adults on their way south to spawn. This is a case where the fish recruit from the nursery ground to the spawning ground rather than the feeding ground.

Plaice of the German Bight and the Southern Bight have been studied by de Veen and Boerema (1959), who found a pronounced difference between the two spawning groups in the length distributions of the winter zones marked on the otoliths (Fig. 16). This pronounced difference between the two distributions suggests that there is little mixing between the two groups. However, plaice tagged on the German Bight or Flamborough spawning grounds return in the following year to spawn on the original ground. No interchange takes place among adults between the three spawning grounds, even after a number of years (de Veen, 1961). The same phenomenon, which occurs for the plaice after two years of age, has recently been demonstrated for soles (*Solea solea* [Linnaeus]) (de Veen, 1961). The possibility remains that a small degree of mixture between the three groups occurs in the recruitment mechanism.

The adult migration of the plaice is of about the same range as that of the larval drift. Adult fish return to the same single spawning ground year after year and do not move to other spawning grounds. Examination of the diameters of otolith nuclei reveals marked differences, and suggests that the majority of plaice spawn on their native grounds. There is a resemblance to the parent-stream hypothesis, but it is

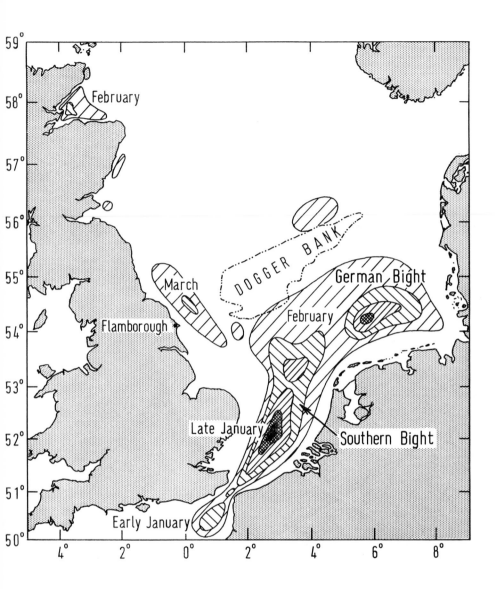

Figure 15. The three spawning areas of plaice in the southern North Sea—off Flamborough, in the German Bight, and in the Southern Bight. The contours represent densities of plaice eggs, and the broken line around the Dogger Bank outlines the 20-fm line. Adapted from Simpson, 1959.

limited to the return of adults to the same spawning ground year after year because the connection between generations cannot yet be established. For the salmon, this connection was made by fin-clipping the young smolts on their way downstream.

North Sea Herring

North Sea herring are predominantly autumn spawners of three spawning groups. Spring spawners and local races exist (Wood, 1937), but they are of small importance. Many complexities arise because, although adults of the three groups probably segregate to their separate spawning grounds, they mix on a common feeding ground. Eggs are

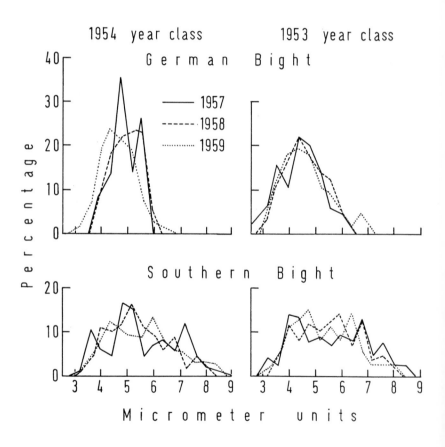

Figure 16. Diameters of otolith nuclei of plaice found spawning in the German Bight and in the Southern Bight. Adapted from de Veen and Boerema, 1959.

laid on grounds of narrow patches of rough sand or gravel inside the
40-fm line and, after hatching, the whitebait (fish of 5–8 cm) are
drifted to coastal areas (Fig. 17). The three groups are: (1) the Buchan,
or Scottish, group, spawning from August to September between the
Orkney Islands and the Turbot Bank in the northwestern North Sea
(Parrish and Craig, 1963); (2) the Dogger Bank group, spawning from
September to October around the slopes of the Dogger Bank in the
central North Sea (Gilis, 1957); and the Downs group, spawning from
November to January in the Straits of Dover and in the English
Channel (Cushing and Burd, 1957; Cushing and Bridger, 1966).

There are differences in meristic characters between the groups in
addition to differences in recruitment, growth, and mortality. A meristic character is one differentiating two populations by the difference
between means of a large number of measurements, like the difference
in mean vertebral count between the European eel and the American
one. The most important difference, however, is in the time of spawning,
because, from year to year, the time of spawning on any one ground
appears to be very regular and precise.

The whitebait drift along the Dutch, German, and Danish coasts in
great numbers (Bückmann, 1942), living close inshore until they
metamorphose. At about one year of age they move out beyond the
20-m line to the Bløden ground (Bertelsen and Popp Madsen, 1953–57),
which is an extensive shallow area east of the Dogger Bank. They remain here until they are about two and one-half years old, and during
this period are exploited by an industrial fishery. About 100,000 tons
(or 2 billion fish) are landed annually at the Danish ports of Thybøron
and Esbjerg and converted into fish meal (Bertelsen and Popp Madsen,
1953–57).

Figure 18 shows how the adolescent fish may recruit to the adult
stocks from the Bløden ground. A group moves north toward the
Norwegian deep water in autumn, eventually joining the adult population in the northern North Sea; a younger group moves around the
Dogger Bank in the following spring, eventually joining the adult
population in the central North Sea (Burd and Cushing, 1962). It is
still uncertain how these autumn and spring groups of adolescents
segregate to the Dogger and Downs adult groups. If segregation were
complete, it should apply as much to immatures as to adults.

Movements of the adult fish are not exactly known. Höglund (1955)
has tagged herring among the skerries on the Bohuslän (southwestern)
coast of Sweden in January and February. The skerries are rocky islets
extending up to three miles off the coast, and the herring are caught
in pound nets from them. Because of their having been taken in these

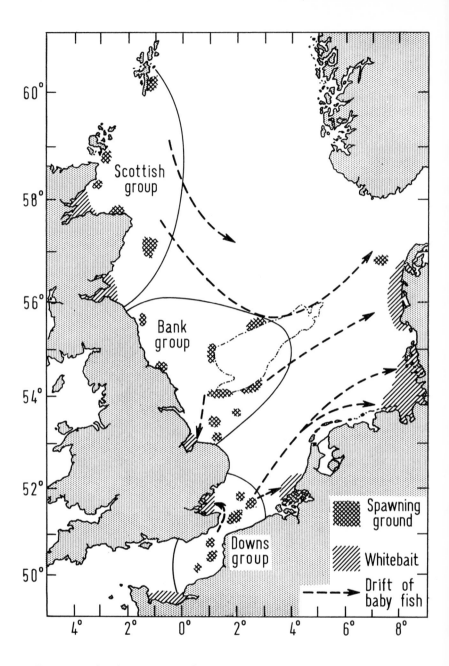

Figure 17. The three groups of herring spawning grounds in the North Sea—
the Scottish (or Buchan) group, the Dogger Bank group, and the Downs group.
The possible drift of larvae is shown by the dashed lines. Diagonally hatched
areas indicate where whitebait are found; the most important are those off the
Danish coast.

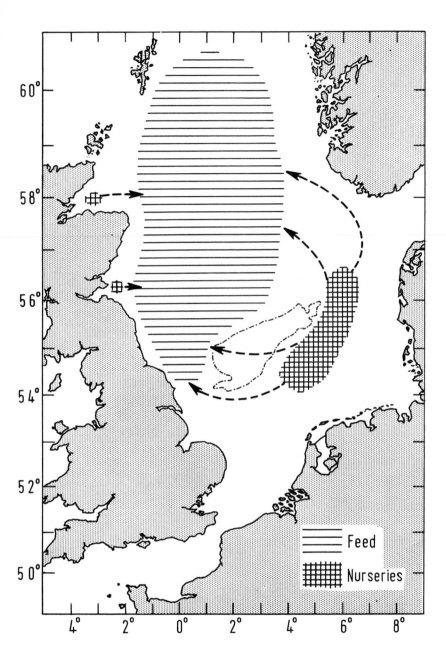

Figure 18. Possible migration routes of adolescent herring from the nursery ground east of the Dogger Bank to the feeding grounds between the Dogger Bank and the Shetland Islands in the north. The Dogger Bank is delineated by a depth contour.

nets, they were in very good condition when tagged. Although Höglund's data are scanty for the winter and spring months, it appears that the timetable of their return was roughly a circuit of the northern and central North Sea (Table 3; Fig. 19). The direction of movement is that of the drift of water around the main North Sea swirl. At three miles per day (Tait, 1930, 1937), herring might drift around the North Sea in one year with some time to spare, provided they could change from current to current. For example, Downs herring live in the main North Sea swirl in summer, but in the Channel stream in winter.

Migratory movements in the North Sea involve three adult stock groups (Fig. 19). Those of the Dogger and Buchan (Scottish) groups are roughly based on Höglund's tagging data and the presence of Buchan fish in the Skagerrak. The presence of Downs fish in the northern and central North Sea has been demonstrated through use of meristic characters and age distributions obtained from fish on the Fladen ground in the northern North Sea (Wood, 1937; Krefft, 1954). Burd (Burd and Cushing, 1962) has correlated the stock densities of two-and-one-half-year-old fish at North Shields on the northeast coast of England with those of three-year-olds at East Anglia. Similarly, he has correlated three- at East Anglia with three-and-one-half-year-old fish at Shields in the following summer, and three-and-one-half-year-old fish at Shields with four-year-olds at East Anglia in the autumn. Hence, it would seem possible that the Downs fish move north and south off the English coast (Burd and Cushing, 1962). The course of the fisheries in the Southern Bight, described in Chapter 1, would support this view.

Adult herring migrate a comparatively short distance, roughly the same as that of the larval drift. The spawning grounds are fixed in

Table 3.—The North Sea circuit of herring as indicated by the recapture of individuals tagged in the Skaggerak

Direction of recovery from Skaggerak	Month							
	July	Aug.	Sept.	Oct.	Nov.	Dec.	Jan.	Feb.
Northeast and north*	1	13	6					
Central†			23	24	5			
South and east‡				1	3			1

* Egersund Bank (northeast) and Fladen (north).
† Gut, Dogger, Whitby, and Western Hole.
‡ Sandettié (south), Horns Reef, and Hantsholm (east).

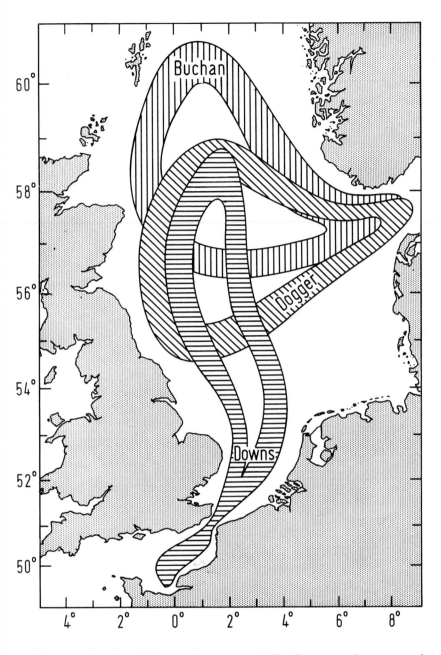

Figure 19. Possible adult migration routes of the three spawning groups of herring in the North Sea. The most northerly one is the Scottish (Buchan) group, the middle one the Dogger Bank group, and the southerly one is the Downs group. Adapted from Cushing and Bridger, 1966.

space and time; this fixity is precise enough to suggest the possibility
of homing without having to provide further evidence. Zijlstra (1958)
has suggested that the consistent difference in vertebral count of
herring between spawning grounds over many years means that most
of the fish return to the ground on which they were spawned. However,
homing cannot yet be demonstrated. But it can be shown (see Chapter
3) that adults of the Downs substock appear to return year after year
to the same spawning ground, once they have recruited to it (Burd
and Cushing, 1962).

Summary

Combining the data for the four fish—eel, salmon, plaice, and herring—we may conclude that the adult migration is of the same range
as the drift of juveniles, at least partially across the Pacific, across the
Atlantic, or across the North Sea. The spawning grounds appear to
be often fixed in space and constant in time. Eels probably return to
their native grounds and so do salmon. Plaice and herring have fixed
spawning grounds, but whether they are their native grounds is not
known.

The reason for ignorance is that the plaice and herring stocks mix
with other plaice or herring groups within their range. The salmon and
eel both return to single spawning grounds, which, in light of the evidence, must be their native grounds. Segregation to their native grounds,
therefore, is not in question.

In the four fish species examined, water movements drift the larvae
to the nursery ground from which they eventually find their way back
to the spawning ground as adults. Because the spawning ground remains in a fixed position, the circuit of migration provides that coherence between generations which is the proper basis of stock analyses.
Some population dynamics can be carried out on year classes only, but
a steady state can only be described properly for a unit stock.

For much of the material in this chapter I am indebted to F. R.
Harden Jones, who has kindly consented to my using information and
data that are contained in his manuscript on fish migration (in press).

3 | The Idea of a Unit Stock

In temperate waters and in arctic waters, a fish stock often has a fixed spawning ground, a single short spawning season, and probably a consistent migratory circuit. In addition, it is a population in which the chances of mating are randomly distributed. Also, spawners do not leave the stock or join it from other spawning grounds to any great extent from year to year. A species can comprise a single stock (e.g., the Atlantic eel), but more frequently a species or subspecies comprises a number of stocks. So a stock is often a unit of population of lower category than that recognized by taxonomists.

In simple cases, e.g., the arctic cod, many of these criteria are fulfilled. Difficulty in recognizing what comprises a single stock arises where stocks mix at some stage in their migratory circuits, as in the North Sea plaice, sole, or herring. If stocks could be separated in the mixed populations, it would be possible to classify each fish as belonging to one stock or another. However, taxonomists do not leave such distinguishing characters unnoticed. The distinctions found between fish stocks are sometimes at a lower level of difference than those found by taxonomists between individual fish. Attempts have often been made to establish such small differences through the use of meristic characters. This technique often fails because there may be a large overlap in the distributions of two populations which is caused not by mixture but by insufficient degree of difference. Statistical methods, such as discriminatory analysis and distance functions (Rao, 1952), can be used to combine the differences in meristic characters found between the spawning stocks of sea fish. In the fisheries, additional differences are due to the numbers of the mixing stocks. Relative abundances of the mixed stocks can be determined if the meristic characters of the segregated spawning stocks are used in combination.

One meristic difference is very clear—the difference in vertebral count between the European and American eel, which is large enough to be clearly of genetic origin, as noted in Chapter 2. The spawning grounds of the two species are relatively close to each other, but they also are distinct, the adults presumably returning to their native grounds (Schmidt, 1922). The migratory circuit contained by the North Atlantic gyre provides the coherence between generations. If spawners do not leave the stock or others join it for a long period, the stock is isolated. The difference between American and European eels is a genetic one, indicating sufficiently long isolation to generate a specific difference.

Where the stocks mix, it is necessarily hard to show that fish return to their native grounds to spawn. A more limited proposition is that the adult fish return to the same fixed spawning grounds year after year. Then a stock may be defined as a population in which the vital parameters of recruitment, growth, and mortality are homogeneous. Because the population should be examined, not in part, but as fully as possible, it is convenient to make the tests of homogeneity on the spawning populations. Then, between spawning groups, a heterogeneity in the vital parameters is evidence of true difference.

As an example, the Arcto-Norwegian stock of cod, a single and unmixed stock, can be contrasted with the Downs stock of herring, which mixes with two other stocks in the northern and central North Sea.

The Arctic Cod

By means of two meristic characters, vertebral count and fin-ray count, Schmidt (1909, 1930) separated the Arcto-Norwegian cod stock from the stocks at Iceland and at the Faeroes. The differences were very much less than in the vertebral count for the two eel species and were low enough to have been generated environmentally. But a small difference of environmental origin, which persists from generation to generation and is caused by real differences in the environment, is as valuable as one of genetic origin.

The large skrei, or mature arctic cod assemble in January and February on the banks of Malangen and Andenes on the northern Norwegian coast before moving southward to spawn in the Vest Fjord (Hjort, 1914). They live in the gullies between the banks at the edge of the continental shelf, and British trawlermen catch them there.

The southward migration from Malangen to the Vest Fjord has been charted in some detail by echo survey (Saetersdal and Hylen, 1959). With this method, a research vessel can be used to survey an area with its echo sounder. Ultrasonic pulses are transmitted to the seabed once a second, and the machine makes a continuous record of all echoes received between surface and bottom along the ship's track. Echoes from fish on the bottom or in any part of the water column appear on the paper record, and they can be marked on a survey chart as the number of fish traces per mile along the ship's track. Echo surveys carried out by Norwegians on research ships off the northern coast of Norway (Fig. 20) show echo traces of skrei from the gullies between

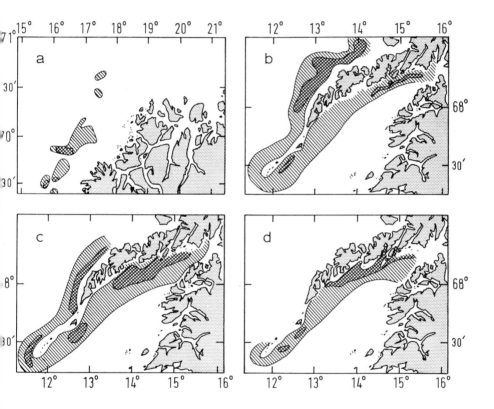

Figure 20. Echo surveys of cod obtained off the northern Norwegian coast as the fish approached the Vest Fjord. The cross-hatched areas are those of highest density; diagonally hatched ones are areas of lower density. Periods of the surveys were: (*a*) 29 January–7 February 1959; (*b*) 8–11 February 1959; (*c*) 25–28 February and 2–3 March 1959; (*d*) 13–15 March 1959. Adapted from Saetersdal and Hylen, 1959.

the banks, where the British trawlermen had been catching them. The
echo traces from cruise to cruise indicate a southerly movement of
skrei from Malangen around the southernmost of the Lofoten Islands
into the Vest Fjord. Echo surveys also show (Fig. 21; Bostrøm, 1955)
a narrow patch of fish traces on the north side of the Vest Fjord off the

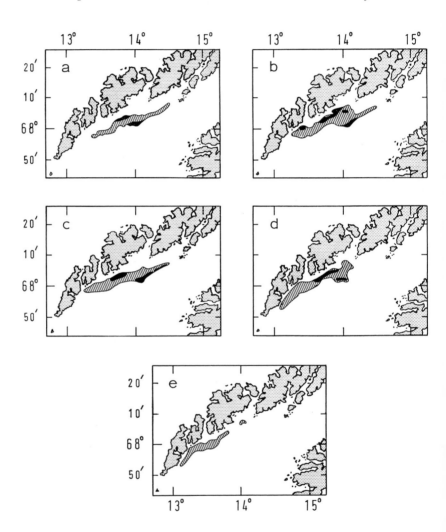

Figure 21. Echo surveys of the "fish-carrying" layer in the Vest Fjord: (*a*)
1–5 March; (*b*) 7–12 March; (*c*) 14–19 March; (*d*) 21–26 March; (*e*) 28 March–
2 April. Black areas are those of highest cod density; diagonally hatched ones are
areas of lower density. Adapted from Bostrøm, 1955.

Lofoten Islands. These fish traces lie in a transition layer between the warmer, saltier Atlantic water below and the cooler, fresher runoff from the land. Norwegians call this the "fish-carrying" layer (Rollefsen, 1955). The male fish arrive in the Vest Fjord first, and spawning takes place in the midwater layer where the fish are caught by drift nets, longlines, and purse seines (Rollefsen, 1954). By the end of March, spawning has finished and echo surveys indicate the northward movement of the fish. They appear to move out around the southernmost island of Røst in the same way as they entered the fjord, but tagging data suggest that some fish move north between the islands (Hjort, 1914).

The cod larvae are dispersed by the West Spitsbergen current to the Svalbard shelf and by the North Cape current into the southeastern Barents Sea (Corlett, 1958). Here the young fish stay and grow into adolescents. These nursery grounds are very close to the adult feeding grounds and the maturing young recruits merely swim into deeper water as they grow bigger and join the adult stocks there (Maslov, 1944).

The range of migration by the arctic cod is demonstrated to some extent by tagging. Hjort's experiment (1914) (Fig. 22) shows the northerly movement away from the Lofoten Islands (at 18 miles per day); later recaptures were taken around the northern coast of Norway. This experiment was conducted in 1911 before trawlers visited the Svalbard shelf regularly, and so no fish were recaptured there from Hjort's liberations. Dannevig's experiment (1954) (Fig. 23), carried out in 1949, shows a much greater range in positions of recapture from an area southeast of Spitsbergen to the southeastern Barents Sea. The range of recaptures illustrated in Dannevig's chart is limited by biological barriers which the fish do not cross (see Fig. 24 and 25). It is the present known range of the arctic cod in the Barents Sea, and the contrast between Hjort's and Dannevig's data shows the danger of relying too heavily on the distribution of fishing fleets to chart the distribution of fish stocks. In another experiment, Maslov (1944) found that cod he tagged in the southeastern Barents Sea and off Novaya Zemlya in summer were recaptured some 300–400 miles westward by early autumn. Results from still later research, conducted by Trout (1957), demonstrated that cod tagged from the Svalbard shelf off Spitsbergen and Hope Island, lying to the southeast, returned to the Vest Fjord area. Some fish were caught in the coastal waters south of the Vest Fjord, but these comprised only a small proportion. The general conclusion from the four liberations of tagged cod by Norwegian, Russian, and British scientists is that there is a single spawning area, which is

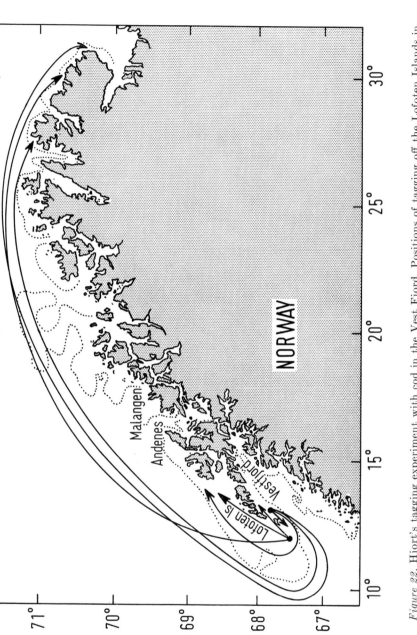

Figure 22. Hjort's tagging experiment with cod in the Vest Fjord. Positions of tagging off the Lofoten Islands in the Vest Fjord are shown as solid circles. The solid lines indicate the direction of movement of the tagged fish to their positions of recapture. The dotted line is the 100-fm contour. Adapted from Hjort, 1914.

predominantly in the Vest Fjord, and that the cod return to this area
year after year from their feeding grounds on the Svalbard shelf and
in the southeastern Barents Sea. No marked fish liberated on the
Svalbard shelf or in the southeastern Barents Sea have been recovered
on the spawning grounds off Iceland and the Faeroes where the fish of
the nearest stocks, separate from the arctic cod, spawn.

The distribution of cod in the Barents Sea has been studied by echo
survey. Figure 24 shows three such echo surveys that were made within
a fortnight of each other to record bottom-living fish (Cushing, in
Richardson et al., 1959). With frequent trawl hauls, the echo patches
were identified as cod. The echoes were counted between 0 and 2 fm
of the bottom, the depth range fished by the trawl. Signals were not

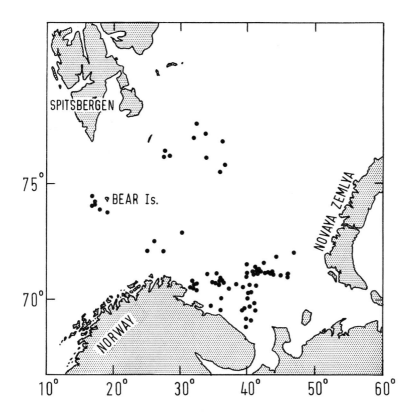

Figure 23. Dannevig's tagging experiment with cod. The fish were
tagged in the Vest Fjord, and the solid circles indicate the positions of
recapture. Adapted from Dannevig, 1954.

recorded on paper, but on a cathode ray oscilloscope, and the fish echoes were counted and classified by amplitude in μv of received signal. The pattern that emerged as a result of the successive surveys indicated that the cod were apparently "thrown" onto the Svalbard shelf by the West Spitsbergen current, and results of a subsequent survey showed that the fish had diffused over the whole area of the shelf, away from the West Spitsbergen current at the edge of the shelf. The spreading of the current roughly follows the progress of the 2° C isotherm on the bottom up and over the shelf. The important point to notice is that in summer the cod distribution is bounded in all four surveys by the 2° C isotherm on the bottom.

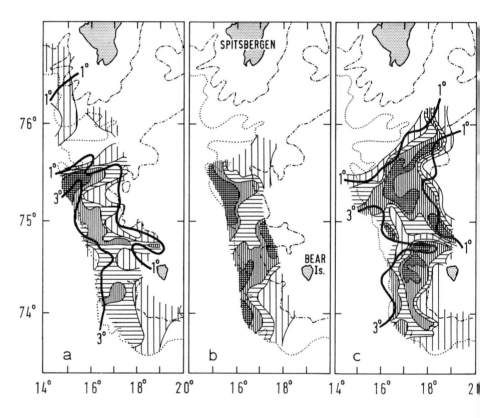

Figure 24. Three successive echo surveys made within a fortnight in June 1956 on the Svalbard shelf. The isotherms of the bottom water moved up the shelf, and with it the echo patches of cod. The four forms of contoured hatching indicate four levels of density, the highest density being shown as cross-hatching. Depth contours are represented by dot-dash lines for 100 fm and dotted lines for 200 fm. Adapted from Cushing, in Richardson et al., 1959

Another isothermal boundary is shown in Figure 25. Four echo surveys, two in spring and two in autumn, were made by Hylen, Midttun, and Saetersdal (1961) off the northern Norwegian and Russian coasts. I have adapted the results from two of these surveys (one in spring and one in autumn) in Figure 25 (*top*) and (*bottom*). It is possible to estimate the size of a single fish from the signal strength of its echo, as recorded by the echo sounder. By means of a paper recorder, the number of echoes from large single fish were counted and charted together in relation to the positions of the isotherms at 150 m. The fish were identified as cod only by their signal strength on the echo sounder, no other fish so large being found in the area. Charts of temperature distribution indicate that, for cod, the opening to the southeastern Barents Sea may sometimes be narrow. Yet results obtained from Dannevig's and Maslov's tagging experiments show that the fish must pass through such an opening both in spring on their way eastward and in autumn on their return.

The tagging experiments of Dannevig (1954), Maslov (1944), and Trout (1957) support the hypothesis that the boundary in the geographic distribution of the arctic cod stock is the distributional range of the 2° C isotherm on the bottom or in midwater. In Chapter 9 some evidence is given (Woodhead and Woodhead, 1959) that the arctic cod is unable to get rid of blood chloride as easily in cold water as in water warmer than 2° C, and that consequently this boundary is probably a real biological one. Hence the 2° C isotherm in spring, summer, and early autumn describes the edge of the range of the arctic cod off Spitsbergen, on the Svalbard shelf, and in the southeastern Barents Sea.

The evidence that there is a single, or unit, stock of arctic cod is as follows. From the spawning ground, fish migrate to the northern limits of their range to feed, and they return a year later to spawn. There appear to be two hydrographic mechanisms containing the stock in the region where it lives: (1) the fish are carried by the West Spitsbergen current onto the Svalbard shelf, and (2) the southeastern Barents Sea becomes relatively more open to them in early summer as they drift eastward in the North Cape current. The same currents carry the larvae to the nursery grounds, thus ensuring recruitment to the adult stock. Evidence of homogeneous recruitment to the stock in the area has been provided by Lundbeck (1954), who found a high degree of correlation among the year classes at Bear Island, off the coast of the county of Finnmark in northern Norway, and in the Vest Fjord. There are certain differences in otolith type from cod found on the Svalbard shelf (Trout, 1957), but fish with both types certainly return

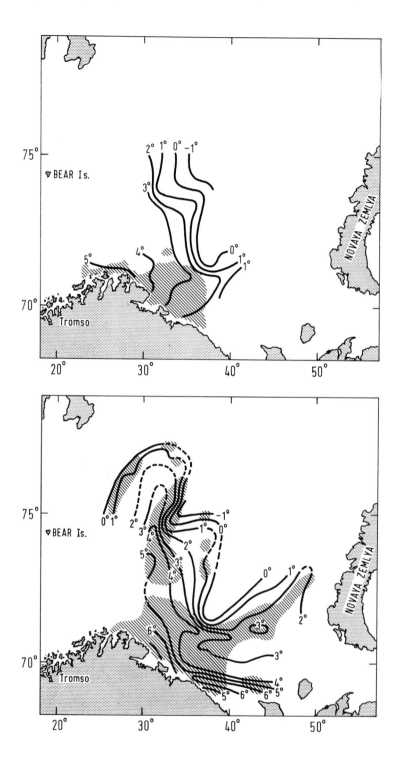

to spawn in the Vest Fjord. There is no evidence of emigration by Lofoten spawners, or any immigration from other stocks. As there is a single spawning ground, there must be coherence from generation to generation; and the coherence is preserved because of the stock being contained within the system of currents. This very simple sum of evidence is the real basis for the stock unity of the arctic cod, and it makes sense of the small differences in vertebral sum and fin-ray count observed by Schmidt (1930) when he compared samples of the arctic cod with those from Iceland and the Faeroes.

The North Sea Herring

As noted in Chapter 2, there are three autumn spawning groups of herring in the North Sea—Buchan, Dogger, and Downs—separated by time of spawning and by ground of spawning. There are also differences in mortality, recruitment, and growth among the three groups (Cushing and Bridger, 1966). In addition, there are differences in vertebral count (Cushing and Bridger, 1966; Parrish and Craig, 1963), in body dimensions (Muzinic and Parrish, 1960), and in fecundity (Baxter, 1959).

Because the adult fish of all three groups mix on the feeding grounds in the northern and central North Sea and segregate to their spawning grounds, it must be shown that adult fish of a given year class return to the ground of first spawning year after year. Tagging of adult fish on their spawning ground would normally represent the simplest method of showing the segregation of spawners from feeding ground to spawning ground, but at the present time the loss of tags from North Sea herring is very high.

The problem can be tackled indirectly by using l_1 measurements from the scales. By magnification of the herring scale with a projector, the distance from the nucleus to the first winter ring can be measured. The length at capture is known, and so is the length of the scale at capture. From the ratio of scale length to fish length, the length at the age of the first winter ring can be determined. This measurement is the l_1, the length at which the first winter ring is laid down. Figure 26 shows the l_1 distributions of year classes within the Downs stock in

Figure 25 (facing). Distribution of cod (diagonal hatching) in the spring of 1960 (*top*) and in the autumn of 1959 (*bottom*) north of the Norwegian coast, as shown from the results of echo surveys. The echoes were from single fish deep in midwater where their distribution is bounded by the isotherms at 150 m. The dashed isotherms are interpolated ones. Adapted from Hylen, Midttun, and Saetersdal, 1961.

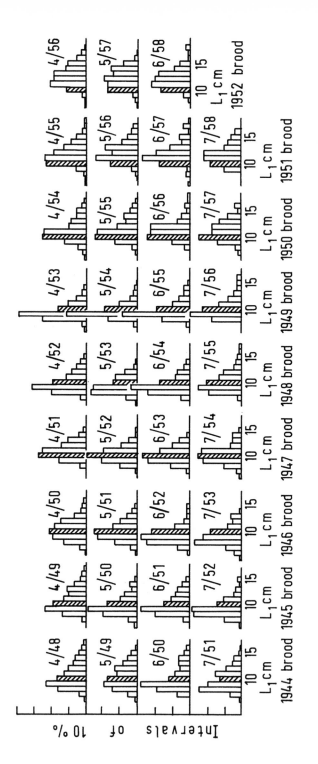

Figure 26. The l_1 distributions of different year classes of the Downs herring stock, expressed as percentage frequency distributions for four years in the lives of the year classes. The 10-cm group is used as a marker to assist comparison between year classes. There is little variation within a year class from four years of age to seven years of age, but there is considerable variation between year classes. Adapted from Burd and Cushing, 1962.

the East Anglian herring fishery. Within a year class, the l_1 distributions show very little variation from the time of recruitment of that
year class to extinction. If mixture took place among the three stocks
on the spawning grounds, the l_1 distributions of the Downs stock
should increase with age, because the mean l_1's of the Dogger and
Buchan stocks are higher than those of the Downs. The Buchan
spawners have the highest l_1's (ca. 14 cm in the mean) and the Downs
fish the lowest l_1's (ca. 10 cm in the mean), with the Dogger spawners
intermediate (ca. 12 cm in the mean). The mere association of herring
having a high l_1 mean with early spawning season and those having a
low l_1 with late spawning season is evidence that the fish tend to
segregate to spawn on their native grounds.

The l_1 distributions in Figure 26 within each year class are remark-
ably consistent, despite considerable differences in mean and in distribution between year classes. If there were immigration of adult
fish to the Downs stock from the Buchan and Dogger stocks after first
spawning, higher l_1's would be expected among the older age groups.
This is not evident. Similarly, if there were emigration from the Downs
stock after first spawning, lower l_1's should be found among the older
Buchan or Dogger fish; from the few data available, there is no evidence of this. Although the evidence lacks the necessary categorical
quality, it does suggest that, after first spawning, the adult fish do
return to the same spawning ground year after year.

As noted in Chapter 1, there are three fisheries on the Downs stock
in the southern North Sea—the East Anglian fishery in the Southern
Bight, the Boulogne fishery on the spawning grounds in the Straits of
Dover and in the eastern Channel, and the Belgian fishery on spent
herring in the eastern Channel and in the Southern Bight. Figure 27
(Cushing and Bridger, 1966) gives a regression of age-group percentages
at East Anglia on the same at Boulogne from 1926 to 1957; in any
year, the percentage of three-year-olds in the one fishery is plotted on
the percentage of three-year-olds in the other, and similarly for other
ages and other years. The slope represents the ratio of mortalities,
Z_y and Z_x; if the slope is not different from the bisector, then the
mortalities in the two fisheries are the same. Figure 27 shows this lack
of difference over a long period of years, with little variance, despite a
range of total mortality from 0.4 to 1.2, expressed in instantaneous
coefficients (see Chapter 4). A similar relationship exists (Fig. 28)
between the East Anglian fishery and the Belgian spent herring fishery
(Cushing and Bridger, 1966). I conclude that the mortalities were the
same in all three fisheries over a long period of years when mortality
ranged from 0.4 to 1.2. This technique for determining differences in

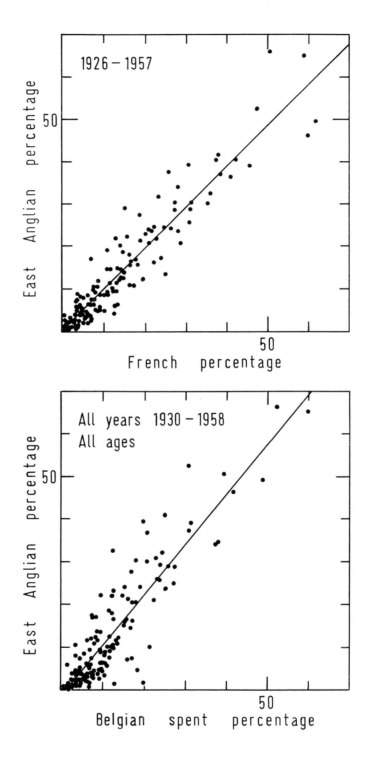

total mortality was used to minimize differences due to availability changes during a long period.

The relationship in Figures 27 and 28 may be expressed formally:

$$\log y = a'' + \left(\frac{Z_y}{Z_x}\right) \log x ,$$

where y is the age-group percentage in the first fishery,

    x is the corresponding age-group percentage in the second fishery,

    Z_y is the instantaneous total mortality coefficient in the first fishery,

    Z_x is the instantaneous total mortality coefficient in the second fishery, and

    a'' is a constant.

When $Z_y/Z_x = 1$, there is no need to transform the data to logarithms. When $Z_y/Z_x \neq 1$, the logarithmic transformation yields a linear regression. Figure 29 (Cushing and Bridger, 1966) shows the regression of age-class percentages in the Dogger fishery on those for East Anglia (the percentages being expressed in logs.) Again, the slope represents the ratio of mortalities, and in this case it is very different from that of the bisector. The conclusion is that mortality in the Dogger fishery over a long period of years was between one-half and two-thirds that in the Downs fisheries. The common mortality rate shared among the three Southern Bight fisheries is contrasted with the difference in mortality between the Dogger and one of the Southern Bight fisheries.

The same technique can be used to examine year-class correlation. If mortality is the same in the two fisheries in the correlation, a plot of the percentage of three-year-olds in one on the percentage of three-year-olds in the other provides an estimate of year-class correlation. Figure 30 shows the relationship in year-class percentages for the same

Figure 27 (facing, top). Regression of age-class percentages in the East Anglian herring fishery on those for the same years in the French fishery from Boulogne. The slope is not significantly different from the bisector; as total mortality generates the slope and as it ranges during the period from 0.4 to 1.2 (in instantaneous coefficients), there are no differences in mortality between the two fisheries. Adapted from Cushing and Bridger, 1966.

Figure 28 (facing, bottom). Regression of age-class percentages in the East Anglian herring fishery on those for the same years in the Belgian fishery off Ostend. As shown in Figure 27, there are no differences in mortality between the two fisheries. Adapted from Cushing and Bridger, 1966.

years (1) between the East Anglian fishery and the Boulogne (French) fishery, separately for three- and four-year-old fish in post-World War II data and for four- and five-year-old fish in pre-World War II data, and (2) between the East Anglian and Belgian fisheries, again separately for the three- and four-year-olds and the four- and five-year-olds. Inasmuch as the East Anglian and the French fisheries share a common mortality rate during the same period (Fig. 27), as do the East Anglian and Belgian fisheries (Fig. 28), the correlation shown clearly in Figure 30 (*top*) demonstrates that all three fisheries share common year classes. When the recruit year classes are put in catch per unit of effort, there is no need to show the common mortality in the two fisheries under

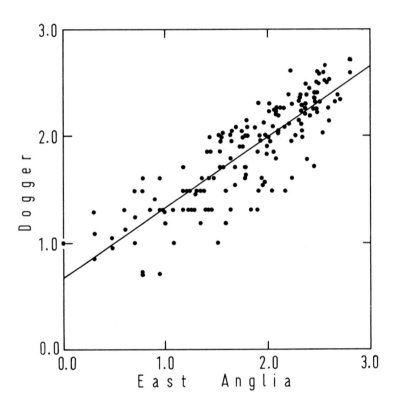

Figure 29. Regression of age-class percentages (in logs) in the Dogger herring fishery on those for the same year in the East Anglian fishery (in logs). The slope represents the ratio of mortalities. The Dogger mortality over a long period of years is one-half and two-thirds that of the East Anglian mortality. Adapted from Cushing and Bridger, 1966.

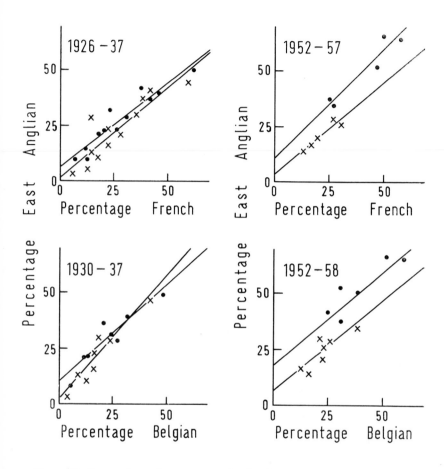

Figure 30. Regressions of percentages for herring in East Anglia on those in the same years in the French Boulogne fishery (*top*). In pre-World War II data (1926–37), percentages of four-year-olds are shown by solid circles and those of five-year-olds by crosses. In post-World War II data (1952–58), percentages of three-year-olds are shown by solid circles and those of four-year-olds by crosses. Because mortality was shown to be the same in Figure 27, this regression must show that the year classes are common to the two fisheries. Similar regressions show that the year classes are common to the East Anglian fishery and the Belgian spent herring fishery (*bottom*). Adapted from Cushing and Bridger, 1966.

consideration. Between the East Anglian fishery and the Belgian spent herring fishery, there is a clear correlation in the catches per unit effort of recruit year classes over a long period of years (Fig. 31; Cushing and Bridger, 1966). Thus, the conclusion is that the three Southern Bight fisheries are fed by the same year classes.

In contrast, the total recruitment to the Buchan, Dogger, and Downs stocks shows no correlation between any of the three in any combination. Total recruitment is calculated from

$$R_3 = n_3 + (n_4 - n_3e^{-Zt})e^{Mt} + (n_5 - n_4e^{-Zt})e^{2Mt}, \tag{2}$$

where n_3 is the catch per effort, or stock density, of three-year-old recruits, the first recruiting age group,

n_4 and n_5 are catches per effort, or stock density, of four- and five-year-old fish, respectively,

Z is the total mortality rate,

t is time, one year,

M is the natural mortality rate (estimated as 0.2 in Cushing and Bridger, 1966), and

R_3 is the stock density of three-year-old fish that will recruit to the fishery at three, four, and five years of age, i.e., total recruitment.

The lack of correlation in total recruitment between the three spawning groups in the North Sea (Fig. 32; Cushing and Bridger, 1966) is in sharp contrast with the strong year-class correlation between the three Downs fisheries in the Southern Bight and eastern Channel.

Within the Southern Bight, there are three fisheries with common year classes, common mortality, and, incidentally, a common growth rate. The three vital parameters in the Southern Bight fisheries exploiting the Downs stock are distinct from those in the fisheries exploiting the Buchan and Dogger stocks. It is possible that there are subpopulations within the Southern Bight group. There are two subsidiary spawning grounds in the Downs group, the first at Sandettié in the Straits of Dover and the second at Ailly in the eastern Channel (Ancellin and Nédelèc, 1959). The vertebral count at Sandettié averages 56.50–56.60 (Ancellin, 1956) whereas that at Ailly averages 56.60–56.70 (Ancellin, 1956). It is a very small difference compared with that between the American and European eels, but it is consistent and persistent for a long period. Le Gall (1935) made many body measurements on samples of fish from the two spawning grounds, but found no differences except in vertebral count. He also compared the percentages of age-class distribution for a seven-year period between the

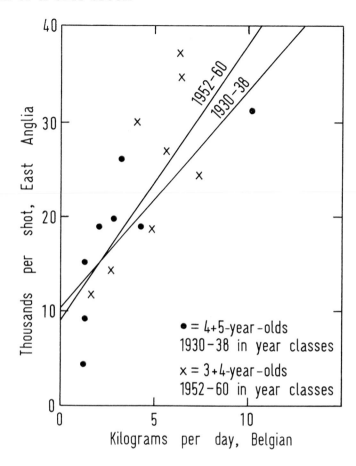

Figure 31. Regressions of recruit year classes of herring in East
Anglia on those in the Belgian Ostend fishery. This material is
presented as catch per effort (a shot being a measure of effort),
and again shows that year classes are common to the two fisheries.
Adapted from Cushing and Bridger, 1966.

two grounds and found them to be the same. The vital parameters that
are common to the two subsidiary spawning grounds suggest that the
single Downs stock has two spawning grounds. The difference in vertebral count between them suggests that they segregate to each ground.

The three groups mix on the feeding grounds in the northern and
central North Sea, and appear to segregate to spawning grounds which
are very localized. The spawning grounds are very small but are nearly
always in the same place. That near the Sandettié Light Vessel is

about 2 miles long and 500 yards wide, and the size of all others in the North Sea appears to be of the same order. There is little evidence that these grounds have shifted since trawlers discovered them between 1930 and 1950. The fact that the herring return to them within a week or so of the same dates each year suggests that they return to the ground of their first spawning. In support of this conclusion is the further evidence that l_1 distributions remain the same throughout the life of a year class and that vital parameters are homogeneous. It is possible that the herring return to their native grounds, but the evidence is lacking.

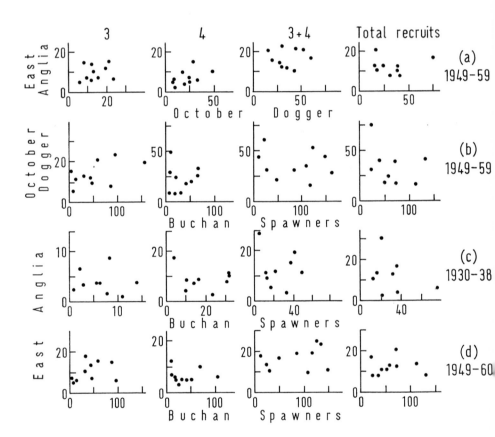

Figure 32. The lack of correlation in recruitment (in stock density) between East Anglia, Dogger, and Buchan spawning groups of herring, at three years of age, four years of age, three and four years of age, and at total recruitment. Adapted from Cushing and Bridger, 1966.

Discussion

The arctic cod is clearly contained within the current systems in which it chooses to live. There is a single but perhaps extensive spawning ground, and there is no problem of mixing with other stocks. The Buchan and Dogger groups of herring have been shown by tagging experiments (Höglund, 1955) to move around the North Sea in the same direction as the main North Sea swirl (Böhnecke, 1922; Tait, 1930, 1937). The three groups of North Sea herring mix on the feeding ground, and probably segregate to their spawning grounds.

There is no positive evidence of coherence between generations in either the arctic cod or the North Sea herring. As no other cod stocks live close to that of the arctic cod and as the fish return to their single spawning ground each year, coherence need not be questioned. The three groups of North Sea herring mix on the feeding grounds, and so the coherence between generations is justifiably questioned. A limited definition of a unit stock can be used—that year classes recruiting to a given spawning ground appear to return to it until they die. For Pacific salmon the question of coherence has been answered in the demonstration of the parent-stream hypothesis. Until recently, it was assumed that the North Sea plaice and sole populations were unit stocks, at least in the southern and central North Sea. The Dutch tagging experiments, described in Chapter 2 (de Veen, 1961), show that there are three groups of plaice within this area, and that the adults return to the same spawning grounds year after year. Here the limited definition of a unit stock used above for the herring would be of value until the point of coherence could or could not be shown.

The most important problem to be solved for plaice and herring of the North Sea is that of mixing. Rollefsen (1934) has separated the fjord cod in the Vest Fjord from the arctic cod by means of differences in the character of the otoliths, but this technique has not yet been applied successfully elsewhere. The obvious way is to tag fish on the spawning grounds, and the mixing rate is then determined by the proportion of each set of "spawning" tags recovered on the feeding ground. North Sea herring cannot yet be tagged effectively enough to achieve this purpose.

Biochemical methods have been used in recent years for differentiating stocks. Some differences of biochemical origin are genetically determined. If stocks were distinct, isolated, and coherent from generation to generation, one would expect genetic differences to arise and some to be detected by biochemical means. Dannevig (1956) has shown that there are marked differences in muscle amino acids between the Skagerrak cod and the Vest Fjord cod. However, it is possible that the amino-acid composition of muscles is affected by the nature of the food. Hence, the difference between the Skagerrak and Vest Fjord cod might only be a phenotypic one caused by different diets. Differences in antigenic properties have been found between stocks of goldfish, *Carassius auratus* Linnaeus (Hildemann, 1956), tuna (J. E. Cushing, 1956), salmon (Ridgway, J. E. Cushing, and Durall, 1958), herring (Sindermann and Mairs, 1959), and of redfish, *Sebastes marinus* Linnaeus, *S. viviparus* Krøyer, and *S. mentella* Travin (Sindermann, 1961). It is well known that many antigenic properties are genetically determined. Recently Sick (1962) has introduced zone electrophoresis for the analysis of blood. The hemoglobin proteins migrate to different degrees in an electric field, and so can be separated. Sick has also shown that these properties are genetically determined. The major hope of biochemical methods lies in the possibility that individual fish of different stocks are distinguishable in a mixed fishery.

The ideal unit stock has a single spawning ground to which the adults return year after year. It is contained within one or more current systems used by the stock to maintain it in the same geographical area. The migration circuit is the means by which this delimitation is achieved and by which the stock maintains its coherence from generation to generation. When mixture takes place, coherence needs to be shown and cannot be assumed.

When only meristic characters are available, fish of different stocks in a mixed fishery can only be separated by the combination of meristic characters. This is achieved by means of discriminatory functions (Fisher, 1936) or by means of distance functions (Rao, 1952). The techniques are effective so long as the differences in the meristic characters are sufficient. Fukuhara et al. (1962) have classified red salmon of Asian and American origin in the open Pacific. The error of misclassification was about 23 per cent, with seven meristic characters combined. Margolis et al. (1966) have used the same method for the sockeye in the open ocean, in combination with tagging observations, scale measurements, and the distribution of parasites. The error of misclassification was lower, and the discriminatory analysis, together with the equally powerful method of scale analysis, provided a clear separation of sockeye stocks in the North Pacific. Because an area of overlap remains between the Asian and American stocks, the International North Pacific Fisheries Commission has been unable to agree on a north-and-south dividing line.

4 | Measurement of Abundance

In fisheries biology, the basic measure of abundance is the catch per unit of effort, or stock density. If a trawler catches many fish in a given area, there are many fish in that part of the sea; if its catch is small, there are few. Such sampling is used in many studies outside the field of fisheries biology. The essential mathematics of fisheries biology shows how the catch per unit of effort is used as an index of the stock in the sea, and how it reflects the limitations of this index of abundance.

Catch per Unit of Effort as an Index of Stock in Numbers or in Weight

The following treatment is taken from Beverton and Holt (1957). From the growth rates and death rates of the stock, an equation is derived which relates catch (or yield per recruit) to fishing mortality. Fishing mortality is assumed to be proportionally related to fishing intensity (or fishing effort per unit area), so the equation can be adapted to relate catch to fishing intensity. Similarly, catch per unit of fishing mortality (or catch per unit of effort) can be related to stock. The equations will first be derived in respect to numbers in the stock.

Consider the number of fish in the sea, the stock of fish, the natural unit of population. If the stock is to remain the same in size, the numbers recruiting to it must equal the numbers dying. Let the number of recruits entering the fishery be R'. After one year,

$$N_1 = R'e^{-Z}, \tag{3}$$

where N_1 is the number of fish in the year class at the end of one year's fishing, and

Z is the instantaneous coefficient of total mortality.

In the year class, the number dying in the first year is

$$R' - N_1 = R' - R'e^{-Z} = R'(1 - e^{-Z}) . \tag{4}$$

The mortality rate, Z, can be separated into two parts:

$$Z = F + M \tag{5}$$

where F is the instantaneous coefficient of fishing mortality, and
M is the instantaneous coefficient of natural mortality.
The proportion of deaths from fishing to total deaths is given as F/Z.
If the number dying in the first year of the year class is

$$R'(1 - e^{-Z}) ,$$

the number caught is

$$\frac{FR'}{Z} \left(1 - e^{-Z}\right) = R'E ,$$

where E is the rate of exploitation,

$$E = \frac{F}{Z} \left(1 - e^{-Z}\right) .$$

Similarly, after λ years,

$$N_\lambda = R'e^{-Z\lambda} ,$$

and the catch after λ years is

$$\frac{FR'}{Z} \left(1 - e^{-Z\lambda}\right) ,$$

where λ is the fishable lifespan in years between recruitment and
extinction.
This expression represents the catch of a year class living for λ years
in the fishery; then

$$Y_n = \frac{FR'}{Z} \left(1 - e^{-Z\lambda}\right) , \tag{6}$$

where Y_n is the yield as catch in numbers.

If there are λ years in the year class, there are also λ age groups in
any one year in the fishery. If the stock is in a steady state, that is,
R', F, and Z are constant, then the annual catch of all age groups is
given by the same expression $(F/Z)R'(1 - e^{-Z\lambda})$. This is the case because, in all age groups in one year, the same items are being summed,
as in the age groups within a single year class. So the equation

$Y_n = (F/Z)R'(1 - e^{-Z\lambda})$ also expresses changes in annual catches in a steady-state system.

If changes are considered that are due to mortality in the fully recruited adult stock only, it is convenient to work in Y_n/R', the yield per recruit, so that the changes due to natural fluctuations can be ignored. Then,

$$\frac{Y_n}{R'} = \frac{F}{Z}\left(1 - e^{-Z\lambda}\right). \tag{7}$$

This is the equation for yield per recruit in numbers. Similarly,

$$\frac{Y_n}{F} = \frac{R'}{Z}\left(1 - e^{-Z\lambda}\right). \tag{8}$$

This equation, in yield per unit of fishing mortality, is the theoretical expression of catch per unit of effort, or stock density. The expression $R'(1 - e^{-Z\lambda})/Z$ represents the total stock in numbers throughout a year class, or the annual total stock in numbers of all age groups in a steady state.

Fishing mortality is assumed to be proportional to fishing intensity:

$$F = qf, \tag{9}$$

where f is fishing intensity, and
q is a coefficient of proportionality, sometimes called the catch-ability coefficient.

So

$$\frac{Y_n}{F} = \frac{Y_n}{qf}, \tag{10}$$

which is catch per unit of fishing intensity. Fishing intensity is fishing effort, g, per unit area, A, so

$$f = \frac{g}{A}. \tag{11}$$

Because $R'(1 - e^{-Z\lambda})/Z$ represents total stock and equals

$$\frac{Y_n A}{qg}$$

which is catch per unit of fishing intensity, then the catch per unit of effort in numbers is an index of stock in numbers. If the catchability coefficient changes, the catch per unit of effort changes its value as an index of stock. In other words, use of the index of stock density must take into account changes in gear, efficiency, and power of ships.

So far we have considered only the numbers of fish in the sea. However, fish grow in weight during their lives in the fishery, and there are a number of expressions for the growth of animals, all of which describe the decrease of specific growth rate with age (Medawar, 1945).

Von Bertalanffy's (1934) equation describes the rate of change of length with time:

$$\frac{dl}{dt} = K(L_\infty - l) . \tag{12}$$

So

$$1 - L_\infty = ce^{-Kt} , \tag{13}$$

where

$$c = -L_\infty e^{-Kt_\circ} ,$$

then

$$l_t = L_\infty \left[1 - e^{-K(t-t_\circ)}\right] \tag{14}$$

where l is the length of the fish in cm,
       L_∞ is the asymptotic length of the fish,
       K is the rate at which length reaches the asymptote,
       c is a constant of integration, and
       t is time.

This derivation is from Gulland (1964).

From estimates of length for age, the constants may be extracted as follows. The yearly increment of length, $l_{t+1} - l_t$ is plotted on length l, where l_{t+1} is length at age $t + 1$ and l_t is length at age t. The slope of the line is $e^{-K} - 1$ and the intercept on the abscissa is L_∞. The equation of the line is

$$l_{t+1} - l_t = (L_\infty - l_t)(1 - e^{-Kt}) \tag{15}$$

Once the slope is fitted to the data by a least squares method, L_∞ can be estimated from the intercept on the abscissa. Another form of Equation (15) is expressed in the Ford–Walford plot (Walford, 1946), where l_{t+1} is plotted on l_t; Ricker (1958) discusses certain cases in which the data can yield biased estimates of the constants. In weight,

$$W_t = W_\infty \left[1 - e^{-K(t-t_\circ)}\right]^3 , \tag{16}$$

where W_t is the weight at a time t, and
       W_∞ is the asymptotic weight.

In order to deal with numbers in the stock and their weight, an equation of the following general form can be used.

$$Y_w = Y_n \overline{W}_t , \qquad (17)$$

where Y_w is the catch in weight,
$\quad Y_n$ is the catch in numbers, and
$\quad \overline{W}_t$ is the mean weight of the fish at a time t.

If Equation (16) is expanded, the subsequent equations can be developed to describe the changes in numbers and weight with time.

$$W_t = W_\infty \sum_{n=0}^{n=3} \Omega_n e^{-nK(t-t_o)} , \qquad (18)$$

where Ω_0 is $+1$,
$\quad \Omega_1$ is -3,
$\quad \Omega_2$ is $+3$,
$\quad \Omega_3$ is -1, and
$\quad \Omega_n$ is the summation constant used in the expansion of the cubic equation.

In Equation (3), the change in numbers is described with time, and only one exponent, the total mortality rate, has been used. With weight is added another exponent, K, which does not vary with time in the same way as Z. The two exponents must be combined in such a way that the rate of change of catch can be described with respect to time.

$$\frac{dY_w}{dt} = FR'W_\infty e^{-Z(t-t_{\rho'})} \sum_{n=0}^{n=3} \Omega_n e^{-nK(t-t_o)} , \qquad (19)$$

where $t_{\rho'}$ is the age of recruitment to the fishery.
After grouping the time terms

$$\frac{dY_w}{dt} = FR'W_\infty e^{Z t_{\rho'}} \sum_{n=0}^{n=3} e^{nK t_o - (Z+nK) t}$$

and integrating from $t_{\rho'}$ to t_λ ,

$$Y_w = FR'W_\infty e^{Z t_{\rho'}} \sum_{n=0}^{n=3} \Omega_n e^{nK t_o} \int_{t_{\rho'}}^{t_\lambda} e^{-(Z+nK) t} dt$$

$$= FR'W_\infty \sum_{n=0}^{n=3} \frac{\Omega_n e^{-nK(t_{\rho'}-t_o)}}{Z+nK} \left[1 - e^{-(Z+nK)\lambda} \right] . \qquad (20)$$

Again, yield per recruit is expressed as Y_w/R'; catch per effort in weight is expressed as Y_w/F, or

$$\frac{Y_w}{F} = R'W_\infty \sum_{n=0}^{n=3} \frac{\Omega_n e^{-nK(t_{p'}-t_0)}}{Z + nK}\left[1 - e^{-(Z+nK)\lambda}\right] = \overline{P}_w, \qquad (21)$$

where $\overline{P}_w$ is the average stock in weight.
In other words, the catch per effort in weight,

$$\frac{Y_w}{F} = \overline{P}_w,$$

is an index of stock in weight. Furthermore,

$$\frac{Y_w}{qf} = \frac{Y_w}{F},$$

and so the estimates of stock density depend upon the catchability co-efficient. The theoretical statement is based on the dependence of catch per effort, as index of stock, on abundance, and this dependence is estimated by the catchability coefficient. In reality, "catch per unit of effort" is obviously not the same index of abundance at all times. Fish may be vulnerable to some gears, yet not to others. They may be accessible to fishing fleets at one season, but inaccessible at another. Changes in a ship's power or in gear efficiency may take place. Vulnerability and accessibility are terms describing measurable modifications of the catchability coefficient.

Availability

Within a given fishery, weather conditions and the behavior of fish are among the factors influencing the catch per unit of effort. Phases of the moon, for instance, can affect catches. Scofield (1929) found that California sardines (*Sardinops caerulea* [Girard]) were caught by purse seines on moonless nights only, and that presumably they could see the nets on moonlit nights. There was also an effect of wind because purse seiners could not shoot their nets when a strong wind was blowing. Silliman and Clarke (1945) analyzed these conditions by multiple correlation, and their adjusted catch per unit of effort is an estimate unaffected by weather conditions. Differences found over a season were rather unimportant, but within weeks they were quite marked. So the California sardines were vulnerable to the purse seine only on moonless nights when the wind was not blowing too hard.

Cod in the Vest Fjord are caught by longline, as well as by gill net and purse seine. The purse seine is probably a nonselective gear, but the longline and gill net are certainly not. Figure 33 (Rollefsen, 1953) shows the length distributions of cod caught by the three different gears in the Vest Fjord. Obviously, length distributions of the cod stock are selectively different for catches made with longline and gill net as compared with the purse seine. The larger fish, caught only by the purse seine, are invulnerable to longlines and gill nets.

Another form of capture depends on the density of fish present. As the meshes of a drift net, or the hooks on a longline, fill up with fish, the chances of capture decrease and so the catch per unit of effort decreases as an index of stock as the density of the fish increases. The effect has been named gear saturation (Gulland, 1955a); as more fish are caught, the remainder in the stock become less subject to the fishing power of the gear.

There are thus three forms of vulnerability—that affected by the behavior of the fish, that governed by the selectivity of the gear, and that working through the numbers of fish.

Either vertical or horizontal distribution can govern accessibility. Vertical accessibility can be readily shown in a pelagic species of clupeid, the sprat. Echo surveys conducted in the Wash, an English estuary of the North Sea, have demonstrated that sprat have two

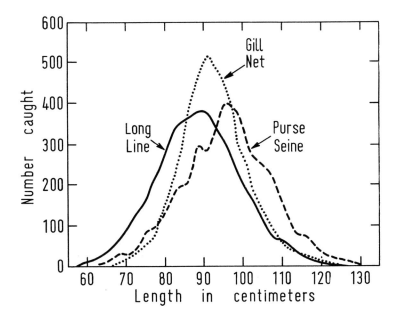

Figure 33. Cod selectively caught by different gears in the Vest Fjord off the Norwegian coast. The length distributions are of fish as caught by longline, gill net, and purse seine. Adapted from Rollefsen, 1953.

distinct layers of vertical distribution—an upper layer of two-year-olds and a lower one of three-year-olds. Figure 34 shows this difference in age expressed in length distributions between the two layers. The sprats are caught by midwater trawls in an area of sandbanks and, because the depth of the trawls cannot be easily controlled, fishermen do not like to tow them too deeply. The histograms show length distributions sampled by a trawl from a research vessel; distribution from the commercial fishery is shown at the bottom of the figure. Hence, the trawls catch only the fish in the top layer, and so only the two-year-old fish are accessible to the fishery (P. O. Johnson, *personal communication*).

A horizontal form of accessibility is found in the Pacific Ocean. Americans fish for albacore by chumming (where live bait is tossed over the side and everyone angles among it) and by purse seine off the California coast. The Japanese fishermen exploit what is probably the same stock along the Equator, and again in the Kuroshio (the Black current off Japan) and in the Kuroshio extension, working progressively eastward during the summer (Van Campen, 1960). Each group of fishermen might regard their fishery for albacore as exploitation of an American or Japanese stock. In view of the albacore's life in the North Pacific gyre, within which it makes trans-Pacific migrations, either view is very unlikely. The stock is accessible to one fishery at a time, but it is possible that all the albacore fisheries in the North Pacific should be grouped into one North Pacific stock, living in the North Pacific gyre.

There are two forms of accessibility, in depth and in space. Accessibility and vulnerability obviously must overlap on some occasions and are facets of a more general concept. The word "availability" (Marr, 1951) includes the meanings of both words, "accessibility and vulnerability." This is a useful term not only because it includes the dichotomy of presence and absence, but also because it expresses the possibility that fish can be accessible and still be to some degree invulnerable.

The Use of the Catchability Coefficient

The measure of abundance is based on two assumptions that are of fundamental importance to the population dynamics of fisheries biology. The first assumption has already been noted: $F = qf$ (Equation 9). It is a reasonable assumption to make when trawling for bottom-living fish, which are randomly distributed with respect to the fishing gear. It is also true for schooling fish, so long as they are distributed independently of the fishing gear. But this concept tends to become confused when ships concentrate in areas of fish abundance.

Catch statistics are collected from an area that has been divided into statistical rectangles. Then the mean density in a heavily fished area

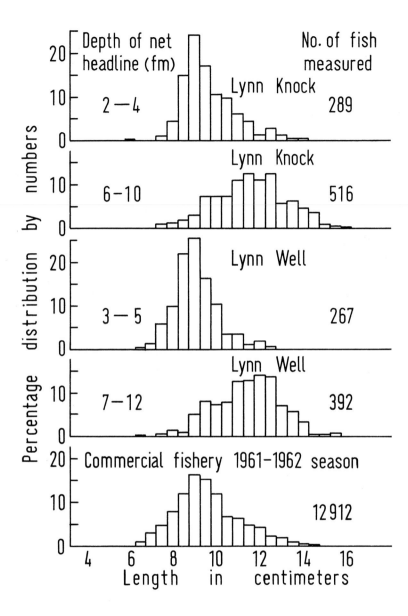

Figure 34. The depth distribution of sprats in the Wash, an English estuary of the North Sea, on 8 January 1962. The fish are vertically distributed in two layers in sandbank areas known as Lynn Knock and Lynn Well. In the top layer at 2–5 fm, the mean length distribution is about 9 cm, and in the bottom layer at 6–12 fm it is about 12 cm. Courtesy of P. O. Johnson.

can be compared with that over the whole area. If each rectangle is
fished, it is assumed that within each rectangle the fish are randomly
distributed. This assumption differs formally from that quoted above,
that fish and shoals are distributed independently of the gear, but in
effect they are very much the same. The concentration of fishing effort
as a consequence of the concentration of fish is expressed (Beverton
and Holt, 1957) as

$$\frac{\sum Y_{ij}}{\sum \left(\dfrac{Y}{g}\right)_{ij}}$$

where Y_{ij} is the catch in the ith rectangle in the jth period, and
$\left(\dfrac{Y}{g}\right)_{ij}$ is the catch per effort in the ith rectangle and in the
j^{th} period.
The effectiveness of this technique in dealing with shoals of fish and
aggregations of ships depends on the size of the rectangle relative to
that of the shoal. If the rectangle is so large with respect to the sizes
of the shoals that there are many separate aggregations of fishing
vessels within it, the method is obviously of little value. If the aggregation of fishing vessels is spread over a large number of rectangles,
then a measure of concentration is being expressed in the catches
weighted by the distribution of stock density. The East Anglian driftermen shoot their nets, which are 2 miles long, over an area covered by
perhaps twenty or thirty small statistical rectangles (each 9 miles×9
miles). The catch data by rectangles can be used to describe the aggregation of the fleet on the shoals. Trawled fish are distributed randomly with respect to the gear, and the effects of ephemeral concentrations are averaged in the course of a year. It is the same for shoaling
fish, provided that the concentrations are averaged for long enough
periods of time.

The second assumption concerning catch per unit of effort is that

$$d = q'D ,$$

where d is catch per effort (or estimated density),
      D is the true density of the stock, and
      q' is the coefficient of proportionality.
In the terms of Equations 3–17, Gulland (1955a) has shown that

$$\frac{Y}{g} = d \qquad \text{and} \qquad \frac{Y}{N} = F ,$$

where N is the number of fish in the stock.

$$\therefore FN = Y = gd .$$

Then

$$q = \frac{F}{f} = \frac{Y}{N} \div \frac{g}{A} = \frac{Y}{g} \cdot \frac{A}{N} = \frac{d}{N} = \frac{d}{D} = q' . \tag{22}$$

The two coefficients, q and q', are the same. So the dependence of catch per unit of effort on true density uses the same coefficient as the dependence of fishing mortality on fishing intensity, the catchability coefficient. Formally,

$$D = \frac{Y}{f} \cdot \frac{1}{q} . \tag{23}$$

The deviation of catch per unit of effort from true density is a function of the catchability coefficient. Similarly, changes in availability are well expressed as deviations from the catchability coefficient.

Differences in availability from year to year can be expressed in terms of q_0 and q_1, where q_0 is the catchability coefficient in the first year and q_1 is that in the second year. For example, $d_0 = q_0 D_0$ for the first year, and $d_1 = q_1 D_1$ for the second year. It will be shown in Chapter 5 that

$$\frac{N_1}{N_0} = e^{-Z} \quad \text{or} \quad \frac{N_0}{N_1} = e^{Z} \quad \therefore \log_e \frac{N_0}{N_1} = Z . \tag{24}$$

Here d_0/d_1 in catches per unit of effort is taken to represent N_0/N_1.

$$Z = \log_e \frac{d_0}{d_1} \quad \text{or} \quad \log_e \frac{q_0 D_0}{q_1 D_1} . \tag{25}$$

So the availability change is given by $\log_e q_0/q_1$, and the mortality rate is overestimated or underestimated to this degree (Cushing, 1959a). Because the proper determination of mortality rate is at the basis of all fishery population dynamics, biases in mortality rate due to availability differences must be traced.

Biases of this character are very hard to detect, and so independent measures of stock are necessary, like those described for the pilchard (see Chapter 1). Stock is then estimated quite independently of catch per unit of effort. Figure 35 shows the relation between the annual egg production of the plaice and the catches per effort in the spawning areas, where the stock is probably well represented. The equation for the lines drawn through the origin in Figure 35 may be expressed as

$$N = \frac{1}{q} \cdot \frac{Y}{f} \, .$$

The slope is an estimate of the catchability coefficient. It has decreased by three times between the period 1913–21 and 1936–50, and so the catchability coefficient has increased by that amount. In other words, the unit of fishing intensity has become three times as efficient between the two periods.

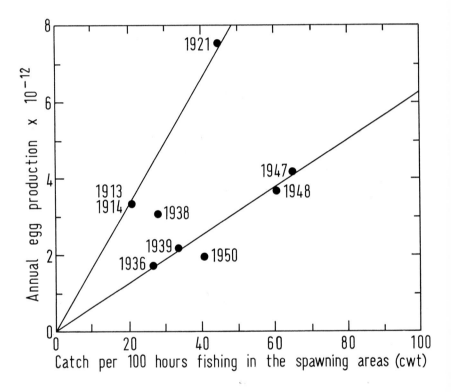

Figure 35. The increase in efficiency of plaice fishing in the southern North Sea. The annual egg production is scaled on the ordinate, and on the abscissa is given the catch per 100 hr fishing in four statistical rectangles over the spawning area. The slope of the line is the reciprocal of the catchability coefficient. Between 1921 and 1936, it appears that the trawlers became three times as efficient in catching plaice. Adapted from Simpson, 1959.

Validity of Catch per Unit of Effort as an Index of Stock Density

The salmon fisheries on the west coast of North America provide a unique way of testing the validity of the catch per unit of effort as an index of stock density. As the fish come in from the ocean to spawn, they are subject to various fisheries in the estuaries. After passing through a fishery, the salmon move upstream to spawn. They are counted by various means, the most common being visual counts at weirs, and the estimate of total population obtained in this way is called the escapement, i.e., from the fishery. The sum of escapement and catch is called the total run, an estimate of stock. Figure 36 shows

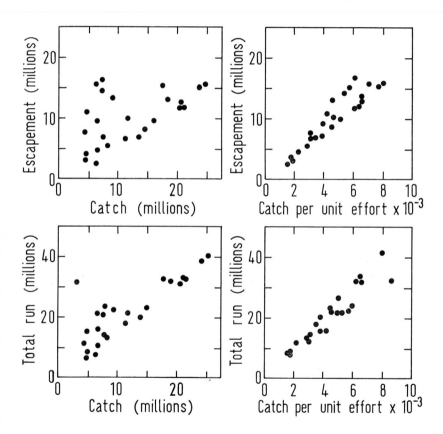

Figure 36. Relationship (1) between escapement and catch, (2) between escapement and catch per effort, (3) between total run and catch, and (4) between total run and catch per effort in the salmon fishery in Bristol Bay on the Alaskan coast of the Bering Sea. Adapted from Tanaka, 1962.

the relationship between escapement and catch per unit of effort and that between total run and catch per unit of effort in the fishery for sockeye salmon in Bristol Bay, off the Alaskan coast in the Bering Sea (Tanaka, 1962). In this instance, the catch per unit of effort is a good index of abundance—one that is closely proportional to the total run throughout its range. But the relationship between total run and catch is a poor one, as might be expected over a long period, as the fishery takes different proportions of the stock from year to year.

Herring lay their eggs on the bottom. On the Sandettié spawning grounds, they cannot be counted readily because the stones on which the herring spawn are too big for the grab. However, herring larvae can be caught and counted, and a relationship established (Fig. 37) between catch per unit of effort and larval abundance (Bridger, 1960). The slope of the line is not the reciprocal of the catchability coefficient, but is a function of it because the mortality from egg to larva is unknown. However, differences in catch per unit of effort are closely correlated with differences in larval abundance. This is an important conclusion, suggesting that the shoals of fish are randomly distributed with respect to the gear. Fish that shoal, despite their highly non-random distribution, can still be distributed randomly with respect to the gear. Figure 37 shows clearly that the catches per unit of effort in the East Anglian herring fishery are probably good indices of stock density.

Echo-sounder surveys can also be used to chart relative abundances in areas of fish stocks in the sea (Cushing, 1952). The most primitive form of survey is that made by recording the presence or absence of echo traces over an area described by the ship's track. A significant correlation exists between the number of traces between stations and the average number of stage I pilchard eggs in the English Channel (Cushing, 1952); hence, it is likely that the echo traces were produced by spawning pilchards. An estimate of the number of pilchards in each transmission that recorded fish yielded a count of 6,834 pilchards (Cushing, 1957). In the Barents Sea, a different form of echo survey was developed for fish living close to the bottom. A significant correlation was found between the trawl catches and the total voltage received from fish echoes during a trawl haul within 2 fm of the bottom (Fig. 80; Richardson et al., 1959). So with the use of many trawl hauls to identify the fish, charts were made of the distribution of cod on the Svalbard shelf in June (Fig. 24). From the figures, estimates of relative abundance in different areas could be made.

Fish cannot yet be identified by means of sonic methods. The two techniques described have really been developed for use by research vessels to give them the comparable sampling power available to the commercial fleet. Problems of accessibility can be solved with such techniques, but problems of vulnerability require something more than relative estimates of abundance over a given area. Ideally, an estimate of numbers is needed with respect to various gear. For example, if numbers within 2 fm of the bottom could be estimated ahead of the trawl and compared with the trawl catch, the ratio of the first to the second would estimate the degree of escape from the trawl, or the vulnerability (or strictly, the invulnerability) of fish to the trawl. Further, the catchability coefficient, q, is affected by the degree of escape.

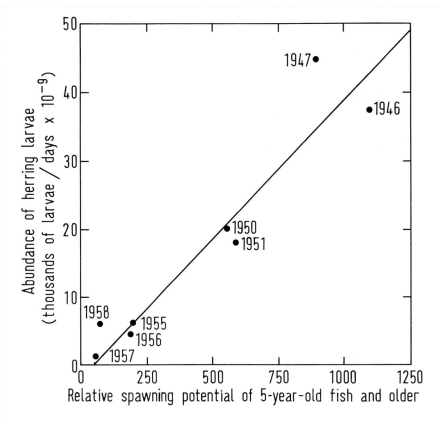

Figure 37. Relationship between herring larval abundance in the southern North Sea and the catch per effort of herring in the East Anglian fishery. The abundance of herring larvae is proportional to the catch per effort of their parent stock. Adapted from Bridger, 1960.

Summary

Starting with stock, in numbers or in weight, equations can be derived relating catch (or yield per recruit) to fishing mortality. Because fishing mortality is assumed to be proportional to fishing intensity, catch per unit of effort is an index of stock. The coefficient of proportionality between fishing mortality and fishing intensity is called the catchability coefficient. The catchability coefficient also relates catch per unit of effort to true density. Differences in availability affect the catchability coefficient in three ways: in behavior, in selectivity, and by gear saturation. Because the catchability can change markedly, estimates of stock independent of catch per unit of effort are sometimes needed. These can be provided by pelagic egg counts, as described for the pilchard in Chapter 1. When used for the plaice in the southern North Sea between 1913–21 and 1936–50, the catchability coefficient of the plaice in the southern North Sea increased by three times, which probably represented an increase in gear efficiency. Results obtained from the same method, in which the larval abundance of herring was used, showed that the catch per unit of effort of herring, a shoaling and pelagic fish, is a good index of stock in the East Anglian fishery.

5 | Estimates of Natural and Fishing Mortality

FISHING is the livelihood of fishermen. It is also of scientific value to fisheries biologists. Fishing kills fish, and both the catch and the number of fishing ships can be readily recorded. Therefore, in principle, fishing mortality should be easy to measure because variations in catch can be related to variations in fishing effort, the total time spent fishing by the fleets. Accordingly, a good fisheries biologist always starts his studies by measuring the effect of fishing mortality.

This chapter examines briefly the estimation of total mortality, Z, but it is mainly concerned with the separation of total mortality into its two components, fishing and natural mortality. If fishing represents a large fraction of the total mortality, the separation is made readily. If fishing represents only a small fraction of the total mortality, separation of the two components is rather difficult.

Estimation of Total Mortality

The sampling system on the quays gives numbers and weights of fish, their ages, the positions and sizes of the ships, and the time spent fishing. Age distributions are then constructed in numbers of each age group per unit of effort, e.g., so many six-year-old cod per 100 hr fishing (of a standard steam trawler). Such age distributions are made by weeks or by months and are averaged for the year. Provided that the biases in availability are detected and eliminated, such estimates are good indices of stock. Then the decrease in stock density (as numbers per unit of effort) of a year class from year to year is a good measure of total mortality. Within a year class,

$$\frac{N_2}{N_1} = e^{-Z} \qquad \text{or} \qquad \frac{N_1}{N_2} = e^{Z} \qquad (26)$$

where N_1 is the catch per unit of effort in numbers of an age group in a
given year, and

N_2 is the catch per unit of effort in numbers of the succeeding
age group of the same year class in the subsequent year.

$$\therefore Z = \log_e \frac{N_1}{N_2} . \tag{27}$$

Total mortality may also be estimated from two stock densities of a
year class separated by a number of years (for example, when $t = 3$),

$$Z = \frac{1}{t} \log_e \frac{N_1}{N_4} .$$

It was shown in Chapter 4 how estimates of total mortality are readily affected by changes in availability from year to year. Fish may be
vulnerable to different gears in different ways. Their vulnerability may
change with season or with area. The stock may be accessible to the
fleets at one season and not at another, in one region and not in
another. Such effects of availability may also be age-specific. In addition, natural mortality may increase with age. The biases in the estimate of total mortality may arise due to changes in the catchability
coefficient, age-specific or otherwise, or to age-specific changes in
natural mortality.

Estimation of Fishing Intensity

Fishing effort, g, is the number of hours or days spent in fishing.
As some ships are bigger than others, the indices are reduced to a
standard size of ship (Beverton and Holt, 1957), or preferably to the
power of the ship (Gulland, 1956). Units of standard fishing effort are
expressed as per unit area; $f = g/A$, where f is fishing intensity, and A
is unit area, usually a statistical rectangle. In the North Sea, a statistical rectangle is 1° Lat. by 0.5° Long., approximately 30 miles × 30
miles. It is the standard area unit used by the International Council
for the Exploration of the Sea; it is larger than that used by the
Lowestoft laboratory in the herring fishery, because the trawl fisheries
are less concentrated. An expression for the concentration of fishing,
which Beverton and Holt (1957) named the "effective overall fishing
intensity," was described in Chapter 4,

$$\bar{f} = \frac{Y_{ij}}{\left(\dfrac{Y}{f} \right)_{ij}} ,$$

where Y is the catch in the ith rectangle in the jth period, and
$\left(\dfrac{Y}{f}\right)$ is the catch per unit of effort in the ith rectangle in the jth period.

Thus, catches by rectangles are weighted by estimates of stock density. Because catch is divided by catch per unit of effort, the expression is of effort per rectangle, or fishing intensity.

Separation of Fishing Mortality and Natural Mortality

There are three methods of separating the two forms of mortality. The first method is to relate variation in total mortality to variation in fishing intensity. The second is to estimate fishing mortality from tagging experiments, and the third is to use independent estimates of natural mortality.

The relation between fishing intensity and total mortality.—The average abundance of a year class in a given year (estimated usually in stock density), the first of two consecutive years, is

$$\overline{N}_1 = \frac{N_1}{Z_1}\left(1 - e^{-Z_1}\right), \qquad (28)$$

where N_1 is the stock density of fish at the start of the year,
$\overline{N}_1$ is the average stock density in the first year, and
Z_1 is the total mortality coefficient during the first year.

In the second of the two years, the average abundance of the same year class, $\overline{N}_2$, is

$$\overline{N}_2 = \frac{\overline{N}_1 e^{-Z_1}}{Z_2}\left(1 - e^{-Z_2}\right), \qquad (29)$$

where $\overline{N}_2$ is the average stock density in the following year,
Z_2 is the total mortality coefficient during the second year.

Since $Z = \log_e N_1/N_2$, as in Equation (24), then the average stock density in the first year can be divided by that in the second, as

$$Z = \log_e\left(\frac{\overline{N}_1}{\overline{N}_2}\right) + \log_e\frac{Z_1}{Z_2}\left(\frac{1 - e^{-Z_2}}{1 - e^{-Z_1}}\right). \qquad (30)$$

The second term in the above equation is the correction term for changes in total mortality from year to year (in this case, from the first year to the second year). So, if Z is constant from year to year,

$$Z = \log_e\frac{\overline{N}_1}{\overline{N}_2} \quad \text{or} \quad F + M = \log_e\frac{\overline{N}_1}{\overline{N}_2}, \qquad (31)$$

where F is the instantaneous coefficient of fishing mortality, and
         M is the instantaneous coefficient of natural mortality.
Since a previously given axiom states that $F = qf$, then

$$\log_e \frac{\overline{N}_1}{\overline{N}_2} = qf + M \; . \tag{32}$$

The fishing intensity, f, has been taken as that exerted in the first
of two consecutive years, because the stock abundance in the second
year has suffered fishing and natural mortality during the first year.
Beverton and Holt (1957) have applied this method to the fishery for
the Fraser River sockeye salmon in British Columbia (Fig. 38). Total
mortality (or $\log_e \overline{N}_1/\overline{N}_2$) has been plotted on effort, g, in gill-net units.
There is only one age group, so the second term in Equation (30) was
not used. The slope of the regression in Figure 38 is an estimate of the
catchability coefficient, q; $q = 0.311$, or 1 gill net generates 0.0012 F
(from $F = qf$). The intercept of the regression is an estimate of natural
mortality, M; $M = 0.648$. In this analysis, the estimate of M includes
fishing mortality outside the mouth of the Fraser River, but the catch-

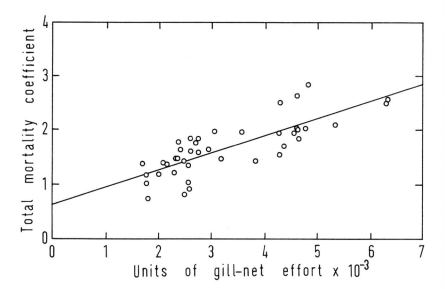

Figure 38. The regression of the total instantaneous mortality coefficient on
units of gill-net effort for Fraser River sockeye salmon in British Columbia. The
intersect is an estimate of natural mortality, which in this case includes the effect
of a fishery in the sea at the mouth of the Fraser River. The slope of the regression
is q, the catchability coefficient, or 1 gill net generates 0.0012 F. Adapted from
Beverton and Holt, 1957.

ability coefficient remains valid for the fishery in the river itself. If there were more than one age group, or if Z changed from year to year, the correction term should be used.* Paloheimo (1961) has shown that if the average abundance, $\overline{N}_1$ and $\overline{N}_2$ and the measures of fishing intensity, are estimated at the midpoint of the year the correction term is no longer necessary. This is because, when measured from the midpoint of the first of the two years to the midpoint of the second, $\log_e \overline{N}_1/\overline{N}_2$ contains equivalent elements of both Z_1 and Z_2 and of f_1 and f_2. When fisheries operate dramatically in brief seasons, it is sometimes useful to consider the years as running from seasonal point to seasonal point.

Tagging as a method of estimating fishing mortality.—The method was first used by the Danish scientist, Petersen (1896). In principle, it is very simple. If 100 fish are tagged and 30 are recaptured, 30 per cent of the stock is killed by fishing. There are two types of error in such an experiment (Ricker, 1948). The first, type A, includes the loss of tags due to immediate mortality and the added loss due to failures of fishermen to report recaptures. The second, type B, includes the mortality of fish due to tagging during the period of the experiment. This form of mortality excludes immediate death in the tagging tank, but includes death due to tagging after release.

Ricker (1945) has given a simple example of a tagging experiment and its pertinent data, using the bluegills (*Lepomis macrochirus* Rafinesque) in Muskellunge Lake, Indiana. Let

$$\hat{P} = \frac{N_m Y_n}{N_r}, \tag{33}$$

where $\hat{P}$ is the best estimate of stock in numbers,
$\quad N_m$ is the number marked,
$\quad N_r$ is the number of recaptures, and
$\quad Y_n$ is the catch in numbers.

In Ricker's experiment, 140 three-year-old bluegills were tagged in early June, and in the ensuing weeks he recorded both the number recaptured and the total catch by scientists, using traps, and by fishermen (Table 4). Working with these data, Bailey (1951) showed an unbiased estimate of this bluegill stock to be

$$\hat{P} = \frac{N_m(Y_n + 1)}{N_r + 1} = \frac{140 \times 728}{29} = 3515.$$

* The plot of Z (from $\log_e \overline{N}_1/\overline{N}_2$) on fishing intensity gives initial estimates of q and M. They are substituted in the right-hand side of the equation given above, (30), to give new estimates of $\log_e \overline{N}_1/\overline{N}_2$, or Z. This process of iteration is continued until the estimates of q and M are constant (Beverton and Holt, 1957).

This experiment has a deceptive simplicity. Recapture data are needed that cover longer periods of time—recoveries from fish stocks that have concentrated to spawn and diffused to feed for one or more years after initial tagging. A theory of tagging is needed that treats the stock of marked fish as a small but representative part of the real stock.

Beverton and Holt's (1957) treatment considers a population, or substock, of tagged fish. Hence their equations are very similar to those used in Chapter 4. The coefficient of natural mortality, M, is extended to an "other loss" coefficient, X, which includes not only the added mortality of tagged fish, but also tag-shedding and the failure to report tags. So the rate of change of the number of tagged fish in the substock of tagged fish is

$$\frac{dN}{dt} = -\left(F + X\right)N, \tag{34}$$

where N is the number of fish in the tagged population, at any time, t, X is the "other loss" coefficient.

$$N_{r_t} = N_m e^{-(F+X)t}, \tag{35}$$

where N_{r_t} is the number of fish recaptured after time t.

Let $F/F + X$ be the proportion of loss by fishing to the total loss in the tagged population. Between t_0 and t_1, the number recaptured, n_1, is

$$n_1 = \frac{FN_m}{F + X}\left[1 - e^{-(F+X)(t_1-t_0)}\right]. \tag{36}$$

Table 4.—Number of recaptures from 140 tagged bluegills and the total number caught in Muskellunge Lake, Indiana, in early June

Fish caught	Fortnights						Total
	2nd in June	1st in July	2nd in July	1st in Aug.	2nd in Aug.	1st in Sept.	
TRAPS							
Recaptures	3	0	1	0	1	n.a.	5
Total catch	35	50	21	10	12	n.a.	128
FISHERMEN							
Recaptures	3	9	8	2	1	0	23
Total catch	120	230	165	39	36	9	599

Between t_1 and t_2, the number recaptured, n_2, is expressed as

$$n_2 = \frac{FN_m e^{-(F+X)(t_1-t_0)}}{F+X}\left[1 - e^{-(F+X)(t_2-t_1)}\right]. \tag{37}$$

If $t_1 - t_0 = t_2 - t_1 = \tau$, i.e., all time periods are equal, then Equation (37) can be divided into Equation (36),

$$\frac{n_2}{n_1} = e^{-(F+X)\tau}, \tag{38}$$

$$\therefore F + X = \frac{1}{\tau}\log_e\frac{n_1}{n_2}. \tag{39}$$

If substitutions are made in (36), then

$$F = \frac{\dfrac{n_1}{\tau}\log_e\dfrac{n_1}{n_2}}{N_m\left(1 - \dfrac{n_2}{n_1}\right)}. \tag{40}$$

Thus, the fishing mortality coefficient is separated from the losses of tags due to all other factors.

A tagging experiment with herring in the southern North Sea was carried out by Ancellin and Nédelèc (1959) in the winter of 1957–58 on the spawning grounds of the Downs stock of the North Sea herring, where many trawlers work. There are three main trawling grounds (which are also the spawning or assembly grounds shown in Figure 6): Sandettié and Cap Blanc Nez in the Straits of Dover; Vergoyer off Boulogne; and Ailly off Dieppe. The tagging was carried out on these three grounds during the period of the fishery. There is a migration by the fish from Sandettié westward, from Vergoyer westward, and from Ailly coastward. However, most tags were obtained from the ground of liberation (where the recapture average was 77 per cent for all grounds). Figure 39 shows the regular decline in number of recovered tags (in logs) with time on each ground. At Sandettié, the numbers recaptured after 10 days were very few, but after 24 days tagged fish were still being recaptured on the Vergoyer ground. The Sandettié Bank is also a spawning ground, and it is likely that much of the decline might be due as much to emigration after spawning as to any other cause.

The fishery on each ground, for example, the Sandettié ground, lasted for 10 days. Because fishermen moved from one ground to another, the whole fishery on all four grounds lasted longer—24 days or more. On the basis of Equation (40), Table 5 gives estimates of the

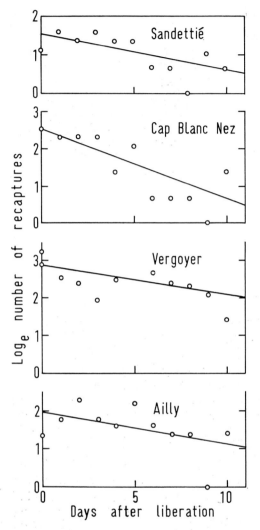

Figure 39. Regressions of log number of recaptures of southern North Sea herring on time elapsed between liberation and recapture for each of the main trawling grounds. The tagging experiment was carried out on the Downs herring stock in the winter of 1957–58. Adapted from Ancellin and Nédelèc, 1959.

coefficient of fishing mortality for durations of 10 and 24 days. As fish did move from one ground to another, the 10-day estimate is an underestimate of the fishing mortality, but the 24-day estimate is an overestimate, because 77 per cent of the tagged fish were recovered from the position of liberation.

The herring catch in the eastern Channel in 1957–58 was 51,190 tons. If the midpoint of the estimates for the two periods is taken, then the effort involved in catching about 50,000 tons generated a fishing mortality rate of 0.08.

Table 5.—Estimates of the coefficient of fishing mortality from the French tagging
experiments with herring of the southern North Sea, 1957–58

Trawling ground	Duration of fishery	
	10 days	24 days
Sandettié	0.034	0.082
Cap Blanc Nez	0.071	0.170
Vergoyer	0.058	0.139
Ailly	0.031	0.074
Average	0.049	0.116

In another experiment, Dickie (1963) tagged cod in the Gulf of
St. Lawrence, which were caught by handline and by otter trawl, a
large triangular bag towed along the seabed to catch fish living near
the bottom. Figure 40 shows the decline in numbers of marked cod
recaptured during a period of four and one-half years after tagging.
Each line represents the logarithmic decline in numbers of a length
group, the smallest fish being the most abundantly distributed throughout the period.

In an extension of the argument in Equation (36), the number of
fish recaptured at time t, n_1 is

$$n_1 = JHN_m \frac{F}{F + X}\left[1 - e^{-(F+X)(t_1-t_0)}\right], \qquad (41)$$

where H is the fraction of tagged fish that survive, and
         J is the fraction of total recaptures reported.
The product JH represents Ricker's (1948) type A errors in initial
losses of tagged fish due to immediate mortality and the losses represented by the failure of fishermen and others in markets and processing
industries to report tagged fish, both of which could bias the estimate
of F.

In a time series, as shown in Figure 41 below,

$$\log n_1 = \log JH + \log N_m + \log \frac{F}{F + X}\left[1 - e^{-(F+X)t}\right] \qquad (42)$$

or $\log n_1 = \log JH + \log N_m + \log S,$

where $$S = \frac{F}{F + X}\left[1 - e^{-(F+X)t}\right].$$

With two sets of releases over the same time period (as, for example, two of the different length groups in Figure 41, n_1', and n_1),

$$\log n_1 - \log n_1' = \log JH - \log J'H' + \log N_m - \log N_m' . \quad (43)$$

In such an equation, n_1, n_1', N_m, and N_m' are known. If JH is set at unity, the relative type A errors between the two sets of release groups can be determined. Such a method removes some of the biases in the estimates of F, thus pointing the way toward improved tagging techniques. In Dickie's method, the type B error, or the mortality of tagged fish due to tagging, can be estimated by differences in the slopes of the log numbers of recaptures on time. The experiment is designed to

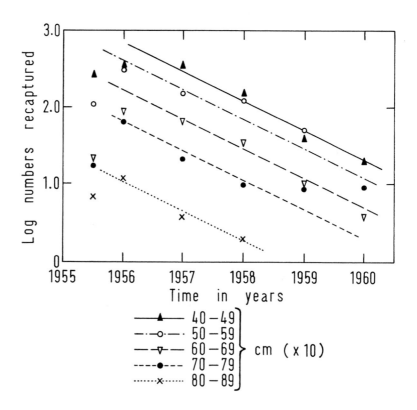

Figure 40. Regressions of log numbers of recaptures on time (log n_t) of different length groups of cod in the Gulf of St. Lawrence. From the analysis of data of this type, relative estimates of Ricker's type A and type B errors can be made; see text. Adapted from Dickie, 1963.

compare mortalities between batches released at the same time and place, but differing by a single factor such as length, age, or sex.

Gulland (1963) has pointed out that there is a dilemma in the use of data from tagging experiments. Because fish die from the very act of tagging, the best estimates of death rate in a time series of recaptures would be those made closest to the time of tagging. Because of the mixing of tagged fish with untagged ones, the best estimates are those later in the time series when mixing is complete. Because of the latter bias, the estimated fishing mortality is never really that of the stock. Gulland has suggested that the use of tag returns per unit of effort, in the local area around the tagging point, might be a measure in terms of abundance. Estimates can be made of fishing mortality per unit of fishing intensity which is q, the catchability coefficient. Let

$$\frac{n_i}{f_i} = q\overline{N}_i, \tag{44}$$

where f_i is the fishing effort in area i,

$\quad n_i$ is the number of returns in area i, and

$\quad \overline{N}_i$ is the mean number of fish in the stock in area i.

In other words, the number of returns per unit of effort is proportional to the average abundance of tagged fish in the area. Figure 41 shows the percentage, in logs, of the initial number of plaice tagged that were recovered per 100 days fishing per statistical rectangle in the southern North Sea during the period immediately after World War II. The decline in this percentage with time is due to mortality and other losses. The intercept on the ordinate estimates q, the catchability coefficient, 6 per cent per 100 days fishing per rectangle. (The intercept is the nominal catchability, $n_i/f_i \cdot 100/N_0$, equal to actual catchability, if all the fish survive.) Gulland averaged the estimates of the catchability coefficient for four rectangles, weighted them by the effective overall fishing intensity, and derived the following values of F (from $F = qf$):

$$F = 0.53 \quad (1946)$$

$$F = 0.63 \quad (1947)$$

$$F = 0.71 \quad (1948).$$

In the period before World War II, the estimate of fishing mortality for plaice in the southern North Sea was given as $F = 0.73$ (Beverton and Holt, 1957). The virtue of Gulland's method lies in the direct estimation of q, the catchability coefficient, from the results of the tagging experiment.

Although an average is taken of those availability differences that are randomly distributed, it remains possible that a bias in availability could distort the estimate of q. A further point is that, as the estimates are based on those from statistical rectangles, the overall measure can be a stratified sample of q, if sufficient rectangles are sampled.

Independent estimates of natural mortality.—Independent estimates are additional ones made by using different methods or different assumptions. Independent estimates of natural mortality in a heavily exploited fishery at sea have often been wartime ones, when fishing is so light that the main cause of mortality must be natural. In other words, it is a special case of the method of correlating mortality with fishing intensity. Beverton and Holt (1957) have made such an estimate of the natural mortality of the southern North Sea plaice. The year classes of 1931, 1932, 1933, and 1934 were sampled between June

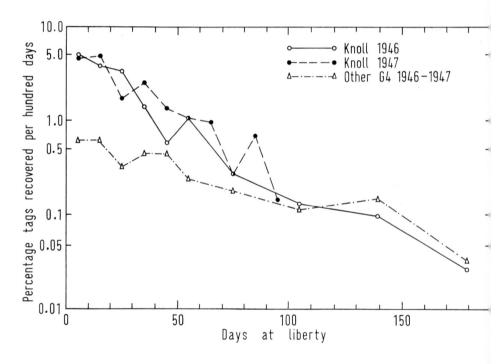

Figure 41. The decline in time of the percentage number of returned plaice tags per 100 days for each unit of catch per effort. The intersect is an estimate of q, the catchability coefficient; see text for derivation. Smith's Knoll is a fishing ground in the southern North Sea; G4 is a statistical rectangle in the same region. Adapted from Gulland, 1963.

1938 and April 1939 and again between December 1945 and October 1946. The mean observed value for the period of almost six years was $M = 0.08$, the estimate taking into account a certain amount of fishing between April 1939 and January 1940. Again, this value takes no account of some zero observations for some of these year classes found after World War II. Beverton and Holt suggest that a reasonable estimate from these data would probably be $M = 0.10$.

The North Sea herring does not live long enough for a proper estimate of natural mortality to be made of trans-wartime year classes. However, two estimates can be used—that from the mortalities of the Belgian spent herring fishery, which continued during the war, and that from catch curves made in 1945 or 1946. At all times, including the war period, the Belgian spent herring fishery exerted a low fishing intensity on the stock, as compared with the total intensity exerted before and after the war. A catch curve yields an estimate of mortality from a single age distribution. The logarithmic decline in stock density from the first fully recruited age group to the oldest age group in the single age distribution is an estimate of total mortality. There are a number of objections to the use of catch curves, notably that differences in abundance of age groups are largely due to year-class differences. However, they can be used with care (see Ricker, 1958, for their interpretations).

For southern North Sea herring, there is a variety of estimates of natural mortality derived from catch curves. Such curves yielded a mortality of 0.32 in 1941–42 in the Belgian spent herring fishery (where one-half of the year classes suffered heavier fishing before the war), 0.21 in 1942–43, and 0.13 in 1943–44. It was 0.22 in 1945 in the Boulogne fishery, and 0.17 in the Fladen fishery in 1946 (Cushing and Bridger, 1966). The average for all of these observations is $M = 0.21$. A reasonable value for the North Sea herring would be $M = 0.20$. Burd and Bracken (1965) found for the Irish Sea herring that $M = 0.15$, a figure obtained from a regression of total mortality on fishing effort. Wartime estimates of abundance are unusual and possibly biased. A catch curve obtained when a fishery is first established, when fishing mortality is only a small part of the total mortality, would yield an estimate of natural mortality. The separation of F and M in a regression of total mortality on fishing effort requires the same estimates at the initial establishment of a fishery, so that a wide range of values in fishing effort and in total mortality can be used. The separation of fishing mortality and natural mortality is the first object of any population study in fisheries research. It is obvious that the right observations are needed at the very start of a developing fishery.

Summary

In Chapter 4, the following yield equation in weight was derived:

$$\frac{Y_w}{R'} = FW_\infty \sum_{n=0}^{n=3} \frac{\Omega_n e^{-nK(t_{p'}-t_0)}}{Z + nK} \left[1 - e^{-(Z+nK)\lambda} \right].$$

W_∞, K, and Z are determined by methods from the ordinary sampling structure; in the same way, $t_{p'}$ and t_0 are found from firm evidence of the age distribution in the stock. The only parameter not determined in the sampling structure is F and it must be found in one of the ways described above.

Fishing mortality can be estimated from the regression of total mortality on fishing intensity. This method requires that fishing mortality is a large proportion of the total and that a considerable range in fishing intensity is available. It can also be estimated from tagging experiments when F/Z is small or when the range in fishing intensity is narrow. For example, the Norwegians have tagged over 100,000 herring during the period of steady fishing in the Norwegian herring fishery (Fridriksson and Aasen, 1950); it can be shown that their fishing mortality was low and that $F/Z < 0.5$. A fishery should be studied when it is in its earliest stages of development. Then a range of fishing intensity is generated, making it possible to separate F and M from the regression. A tagging experiment could confirm the estimate of F and perhaps an independent estimate of M might emerge from the initial stock studies of the fishery.

6 | The Control of Fishing

THE common experience of fishermen who work on demersal fish is that the harder they fish the fewer fish they catch and the ones they do catch are smaller. In 1823, sailing smacks were landing up to 1,000 or 2,000 large turbot (*Psetta maxima* [Linnaeus]) after each trip in the Straits of Dover from the Sandettié Bank, or New Bank, as it was then called; by 1840, there was hardly a turbot to be found on these grounds (Alward, 1932). Fishermen know that the high catches made when grounds are first discovered cannot be repeated. They have named such grounds "Klondike" or "El Dorado." Just as the goldfields were worked out, so some grounds were apparently fished out. Changes took place, for example, in catches per unit of effort as expressed in weight of plaice in the North Sea during the periods both before and after World Wars I and II (Wimpenny, 1953; Great Britain, 1885–1965. . . . Statistical tables). The relaxation of fishing effort during each war period allowed the stock to increase in weight by many times. When peace returned, fishing was resumed and the stock fell to its prewar weight level or even lower. But the fishermen have not readily understood why the fish became smaller as the stocks were fished harder. They believed that the breeding grounds had become disturbed.

The decrease in size of some demersal fish with increased fishing pressure is really a function of their growth pattern. During their lives in the fishery, such fish grow very much; if their lives are shortened by fishing, the mean sizes of the fish become much smaller. Obviously such a state can be cured by reduced fishing. The operational problem is to find the largest catch in weight for the least fishing intensity. The methods are fully described in Beverton and Holt (1957), from which most of the following treatment is taken.

The Yield Curve

The yield or catch equation given at the end of Chapter 5 is expressed as yield per recruit, Y_w/R'. The reason for this is, first, that the very large fluctuation in year classes obscures the catch and fishing relationship in the data. Secondly, and much more important, we need to separate the relationship between catch and fishing intensity from that between stock and recruitment. The latter is a complex problem and very hard to disentangle, but it is described in Chapter 8. Here we are concerned only with the relationship between catch and fishing intensity. Model conditions are constructed by plotting Y_w/R' on F, the fishing mortality. As F is assumed to be proportional to fishing intensity, the curve expresses the relationship between catch and fishing.

Two such curves, for plaice and herring in the North Sea, are very different (Fig. 42). For plaice (Beverton and Holt, 1957), there is a peak in Y_w/R' at $F = 0.2$, and at higher values of fishing mortality there is a decline in yield (Fig. 42, *top*). As fishing mortality increases, fewer fish are found in the sea, and greater numbers are caught. At the same time, the average weight of the fish declines with increased fishing mortality, each fish having less chance to put on weight. The catch is the product of the numbers caught and their weights. The one increases with fishing mortality and the other decreases. So the curve of Y_w/R' on F reaches a maximum value in F. If much weight is put on during the exploitable life span, the peak is sharp; if the fish do not grow at all during their lives in the fishery, there is no peak, the catch rising to an asymptote. For fish that do not grow much during their exploitable life span, the yield curve resembles that for numbers only. In Figure 42 (*top*), the dashed line at $F = 0.73$ shows the prewar yield of plaice.

Figure 42 (facing). *Top*. The yield curve for plaice (as Y_w/R' plotted on F, fishing mortality). There is a maximum at $F = 0.2$. The dashed line at $F = 0.73$ shows the prewar condition. So an increase in total catch of 20 per cent could have been obtained by reducing the number of ships by three times. Adapted from Beverton and Holt, 1957.

Bottom. The yield curve for herring for five different year classes. No peak is found in Y_w/R'; in other words, with increased fishing intensity more bulk weight of fish is landed, but only up to a certain maximum level. The difference in Y_w/R' in the five year classes expresses the marked effect of growth differences between them on the total catch. Relatively, such differences are much greater than those found for the plaice. Adapted from Cushing and Bridger, 1966.

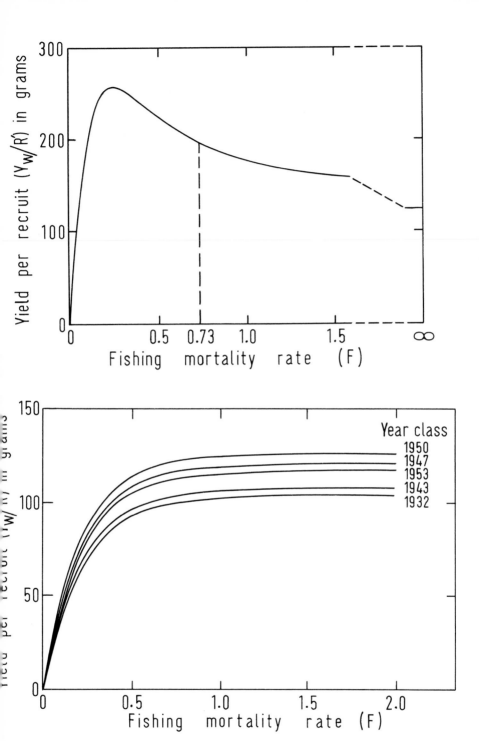

From the figure, it is clear that the prewar catch in the North Sea was only 80 per cent of what it might have been if the fishing effort had been reduced by three times. The calculations were based on an assumed mesh size of 70 mm in the cod end of the trawl. The actual mesh size was probably nearer 50 mm, and so the real state was worse than that shown in the figure.

The yield curve for herring (Figure 42, *bottom*) is quite different (Cushing and Bridger, 1966). With increased fishing mortality, yield increases to an asymptote. There is a theoretical maximum to this curve, but in practice it is asymptotic. The biological difference between plaice and herring is that the plaice might grow twenty times in weight during its life in the fishery, whereas the herring only grows about one and one-half times. Consequently, the yield curve for the herring is very nearly that for the yield in numbers, with, however, an ill-defined maximum at very high values of F. On the rising limb of the curve for plaice, the gain in numbers is greater than the loss in weight as fishing intensity increases. On the descending limb, with harder fishing, the gain in numbers is much less than the loss in weight. In other words, the little fish are caught before they have a chance to grow.

The formal difference between the plaice and the herring concerns the nature of the growth parameters, absolutely in the magnitude of W_∞ and relatively in the value of K. The growth equation used is (von Bertalanffy, 1934)

$$W_t = W_\infty[1 - e^{-K(t-t_o)}]^3.$$

The relationship between K and W_∞ tends to be inverse. If K is high, W_∞ is reached rapidly in time; if K is low, the asymptotic weight is reached slowly. In general, big fish tend to have low values of K and small fish to have high values. The difference between the growth parameters of plaice (Beverton and Holt, 1957) and herring (Cushing and Bridger, 1966) is demonstrated as follows:

	W_∞	K
Plaice	2867 g	0.095
Herring	197–224 g	0.31–0.57

The Effect of Natural Mortality and Density-Dependent Growth

Different natural mortalities affect the yield curves for plaice (Fig. 43). As noted in Chapter 5, Beverton and Holt (1957) have estimated the true natural mortality for plaice (as used in Fig. 42, *top*) at 0.10.

When $M = 0.05$, the peak of the curve is exaggerated as compared
with that for $M = 0.10$. When M is high (0.50), the curve tends toward an asymptote, as with the herring. In such a situation, the loss
in numbers by natural mortality at nearly all values of F is so high
that it nullifies any excess gain in weight, which might give a peak to
the curve.

The growth of fish may well be density dependent. The von Bertalanffy parameters, K and W_∞, are inversely related. Assuming K to
be constant, Beverton and Holt found a decrease in L_∞ of about 20
per cent for an increase in stock of six times during World War II for
haddock (*Melanogrammus aeglefinus* [Linnaeus]) in the western and
central North Sea. The model used was that the asymptotic length,

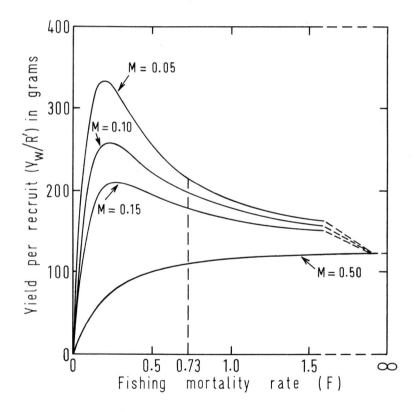

Figure 43. Yield curves for plaice calculated at a range of values of natural mortality, $M = 0.05$, $M = 0.10$, $M = 0.15$, and $M = 0.50$. At very low
values of natural mortality, the peak of the curve is sharper. Adapted from
Beverton and Holt, 1957.

L_∞, varies inversely and linearly with the stock quantity. Figure 44
shows the effect of this form of density-dependent growth on the yield
curves for plaice. If growth is reduced to some extent as numbers increase, the peak of the curve is reduced, which might be expected.
Density-dependent growth has been detected in many freshwater fish
and in the immature stages of marine fish, but it has not yet been discovered in the adult stages. It is probably present, but differences in
growth due to density cannot be readily distinguished from differences
due to other causes. The models are used to show how the relation between catch and fishing might be modified by the density-dependent
growth of the fish.

The Use of Yield Curves in Management

The practical value of these curves is in the peak. Obviously, it is
wrong that fishermen should have to exploit the stock at any point

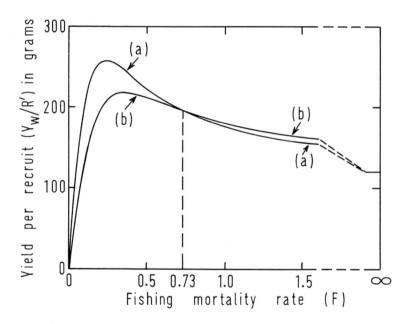

Figure 44. Yield curves for plaice calculated with density-dependent
growth; it was assumed that L_∞ varied inversely with stock density. If
growth is reduced with increased stock, the peak of the curve is reduced, as
might be expected. Curve (a) is that with constant parameters; curve (b)
is that with density-dependent values of L_∞. Adapted from Beverton and
Holt, 1957.

beyond or to the right of the maximum. For example, in Figure 42 (*top*), to reach the point of maximum yield the prewar fishing intensity could have been reduced by three times, with the immediate effect that many companies would have become bankrupt and many fishermen driven into other employment. Therefore the change should be gradual. In the yield equation, $t_{\rho'}$ is defined as the age of entry into the fishery. It is often the age at first recruitment. If, however, $t_{\rho'}$ were to be set at a more advanced age, some small fish would be allowed to grow instead of being caught. Thus, for the same fishing effort, bigger fish are caught, and for moderate increases in the age at first recruitment the total catch is heavier. This goal could be achieved by putting larger meshes in the cod ends of the trawls, thus allowing the small fish to escape and grow.

Figure 45 is a complicated three-dimensional diagram of the yield of plaice at different mesh sizes and fishing mortality rates: $t_{\rho'}$ is shown on the ordinate as the age of entry into the fishery—in practice, this represents the mesh size of the trawl; F, fishing mortality, is set on the abscissa; values of Y_w/R' are described by contours. At a fixed level of F, if too big a mesh size is used in the trawl, only the biggest fish are caught, but as there are not very many really large fish, Y_w/R' is low. If too small a mesh size is used at that value of F, too many fish are caught before they have had time to grow. The greatest weight in the catch is found at an intermediate mesh size. This maximum yield for a given value of F rises continuously to an asymptote as a function of F and $t_{\rho'}$, fishing effort, and mesh size.

The important point about Figure 45 is the range of choice offered in a plaice fishery, because there is an optimum mesh size for any given fishing intensity. The prewar value of $F = 0.73$ is marked on the abscissa. If $t_{\rho'}$ had been increased from age three to age nine by increasing the mesh sizes in the trawls from 70 mm to 180 mm, the possible improvement would have been a doubling of the catch for the same fishing intensity. By opening the meshes of the trawls and letting the little fish grow, the catches are increased. But it is most important to point out that this is best done gradually. A sudden and large increase in mesh size would cause first a decline in catch and then a recovery, because the condition could not be corrected with the existing year classes, and the recovery would have to wait for new broods to grow. What has actually happened is that the fishing mortality rate has become much reduced (0.47; Gulland, 1966) and the English fishermen, at least, search for the largest fish. They are effectively using a high $t_{\rho'}$, much higher than that implied by the mesh size. In other words, they are carrying out their own regulations.

98   FISHERIES BIOLOGY

The examination of yield curves in management has been restricted
to the trawl fisheries. Throughout the North Atlantic the trawl fisheries
of all countries are under the control of two commissions, the North
East Atlantic Fisheries Commission (NEAFC) and the International
Commission for the Northwest Atlantic Fisheries (ICNAF). It is a
triumph of fisheries administration to have made the two commissions

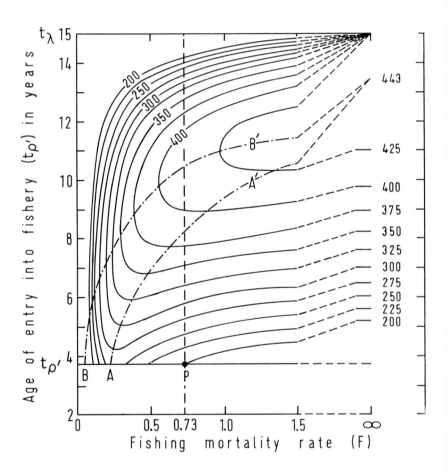

Figure 45. Yield isopleth diagram of $t_{p'}$, or age at first capture, on fishing
mortality, F. The contours, or isopleths, represent the magnitudes of yield,
Y_w/R', in g, of plaice. At $F = 0.73$, the prewar level of fishing mortality (shown
at P), yield increases with increasing age at first capture to a maximum, and then
it declines. The line AA' represents the condition for the largest mesh size and
least fishing mortality. The line BB' represents the condition for the smallest
mesh size and highest fishing mortality. Adapted from Beverton and Holt, 1957.

work and to have ensured that the catches of demersal fish from the North Atlantic are by and large well controlled. In the Pacific, the International North Pacific Fisheries Commission and the Inter-American Tropical Tuna Commission carry out similar functions. Indeed, the Pacific halibut (*Hippoglossus stenolepis* Schmidt) was the first stock of marine fish to be internationally regulated by the International Fisheries Commission (IFC, between Canada and the United States) since 1930.

Heavy fishing has another effect. As fishermen increase their fishing effort, the stock in weight begins to decline accordingly. A curve illustrating this process can be constructed for herring in the southern North Sea (Fig. 46). In effect, this is a curve of catch per unit of effort, or of stock on effort ($M = 0.2$; Cushing and Bridger, 1966). As the fishermen fish harder, the stock in weight becomes less dense. An important point here is that the catch per unit of effort is not only an

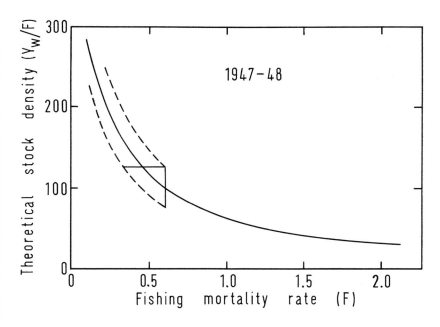

Figure 46. A curve of catch per effort (Y_w/F) on fishing mortality for the North Sea herring. The dashed lines represent the variability in catch per effort due to recruitment only. The vertical line represents a hypothetical low limit of catch per effort, beyond which the fishermen will not go fishing. The horizontal line cuts the curve of catch per effort at a point where the low limit of catch per effort will not be reached due merely to variations in recruitment. Adapted from Cushing, 1959a.

index of stock, but it is also an index of profit. As the stock of fish declines, so does the profit to the fishermen, and Figure 46 expresses this view. With increased fishing, the number of year classes in the stock also declines. Since 1958 the southern North Sea herring has provided the fishermen with essentially a one-year-class fishery (see Fig. 9). The range of variation in the magnitude of year-class strength is high (about $\times$ 10; Cushing, 1959a), and some of this variability would be reduced if more year classes were available in the stock. With no fishing, the coefficient of variation of the annual yield due to year-class variability would be about 10 per cent; when $Z = 1.0$, the coefficient of variation is about 30 per cent (Cushing, 1959a). The dashed lines in Figure 46 show the coefficient of variation in catch per unit of effort, increasing with increased mortality as catch per unit of effort falls.

In the North Sea, the herring is fished seasonally. Scots fishermen join the East Anglian fishery in the southern North Sea in the autumn. If the year class is a poor one in weight, catches are low and the Scotsmen are discouraged from coming in subsequent years, when a bigger year class might well enter the fishery. Then the bigger year class is not exploited as much as it should be in the East Anglian fishery. The cycle gradually reduces the number of Scottish fishermen willing to come.

The only way in which this year-class variability might be curbed is by reducing the fishing effort. There is a low economic level of catch per unit of effort beyond which the fishermen will not put to sea. If Figures 42 (*bottom*) and 46 were to be combined, a reduction in fishing mortality rate from 0.6 to 0.48 would be indicated; catch would be reduced by about 4 per cent and catch per unit of effort would increase by 20 per cent; more important, it would be a more stable catch per unit of effort (Cushing, 1959a). For a small degree of sacrifice in total catch, some stability in catch per unit of effort and therefore in annual profit might be obtained in some seasonal fisheries.

Most regulation at the present time is intended to obtain the "maximum sustainable yield," or the catch at the peak of the yield curve. In some cases, like the East Anglian fishery, a better economic yield might have been taken at less than the maximum. But measures based on econometric values between countries are probably very hard to obtain. In an optimistic view of the future, however, the best yield may be taken in economic terms at a point short of the maximum.

Two Simpler Forms of Stock Assessment

There are two useful simplified procedures involved in stock assessment. One concerns the dependence of stock density on fishing effort.

In the Icelandic cod fishery, as sampled by British trawlers (Gulland, 1961), catch per unit of effort in one year (stock density in cwt per 100 ton-hr) tends to be inversely proportional to the average effort over the previous three years (Fig. 47). There are six age groups of fair abundance in the stock. The catch per unit of effort represents the stock density of a number of year classes; the effort averaged over three years is the mean effort modifying the stock of the six year

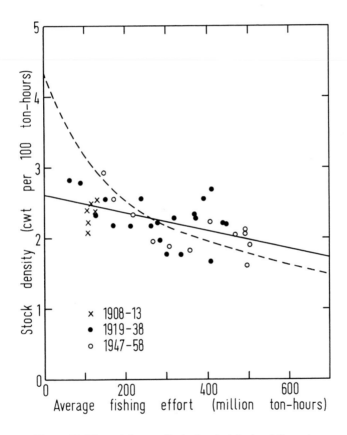

Figure 47. The catch per effort of cod at Iceland (in cwt per 100 ton-hr) and the average fishing effort over the previous three years. Any catch per effort represents the stock density of a number of year classes. The effort over three years is that average effort which has modified the stock of six year classes. The solid line has been fitted by the method of least squares; the dashed line has been fitted visually to the same data to represent the theoretical curve. Adapted from Gulland, 1961.

classes. The theoretical fitting of the curve to the data demands estimates of all parameters, particularly F and M. The least-squares (solid)
line fitted to the data in Figure 47 needs only estimates of stock density
and of fishing effort. The equation is

$$\frac{Y}{f} = \delta - \epsilon f, \tag{45}$$

where Y/f is catch per unit of effort of fishing intensity,
$\quad f \quad$ is fishing intensity, and
$\quad \delta$ and ϵ are constants.

The three-year averages of fishing effort, if taken in each successive
year, are not independent and neither are the corresponding estimates
of stock density. The averages taken at intervals three years apart are
independent and so are the corresponding estimates of stock density.
The yield equation is given simply by the parabola

$$Y = \epsilon f - \delta f^2. \tag{46}$$

The dashed line in Figure 47 is a curve that has been eye-fitted to
the data of catch per unit of effort on fishing effort. The distortion
introduced by using a straight line rather than the curve might displace
the maximum to some extent. In the Icelandic cod stocks that have
been described here, the maximum yield available to fishermen is
beyond the range of fishing effort. The conclusion—that the stock will
stand more fishing—remains true, whether the data are fitted by eye
or by a least-squares line.

Gulland's method resembles that of Schaefer (1954), particularly in
the use of a parabola to locate the point of maximum yield on the scale
of fishing intensity. These methods are useful when age determination
is difficult (as in the Pacific tuna) or when the observations are lacking
(as in the Icelandic cod). Consequently, the effects of growth and recruitment are confused. It might be said that the yield-curve method
ignores the effects of recruitment, but this is not really true. Variance
due to recruitment can be added to any estimate of the maximum sustainable yield. Where both methods really fail in this context is when
recruitment increases or declines with time. An axiom to all methods
at the present time is that, within the range of stock fished, recruitment
is independent of parent stock. In practice, the axiom may be valid,
but there are stocks in which it can be shown not to be true, as, for
example, the Pacific salmon stocks (see Chapter 8).

A second simplified procedure involves the rate of exploitation,
E (or $F/Z \cdot 1 - e^{-Z}$).

$$W_c = E\overline{W}, \tag{47}$$

where W_c is the weight at first capture, and
$\overline{W}$ is the mean weight of fish in the catch greater than W_c.
So to get an increase in catch from a given fishery (Allen, 1953),

$$E > \frac{W_c}{\overline{W}} \cdot \tag{48}$$

This value has been called the break-even value of E. It has been used in the ICNAF area, that is, from West Greenland to Cape Cod in the United States. The Commission has regulatory powers over fish stocks in this area. The value of this simplification is that, given W_c and $\overline{W}$, the range in values of E can be set at which an increase in catch can be expected. If F and M have not been determined, estimates can be made of the conditions under which catch should increase.

One of the controversial aspects of fisheries regulation in the past has been that the increase in catch after regulation has been attributed to natural changes. In other words, the increase in catch was not attributed to the reduced effort, but to a coincidental increase in recruitment. For example, the Pacific halibut stock density declined steadily until 1930 when a closed season was imposed. Subsequently, the stock density increased steadily, even into the 1960's (Fukuda, 1962). Such an argument cannot be answered because the two possibilities cannot be distinguished. But the validity of the theoretical case must then be denied, and the increase in catch must be attributed to chance. It is rather unlikely that a coincidental increase in catch due to a recruitment change should be of the same order as an increase due to relaxation of effort.

For the regulation of demersal fish in the North Sea, it is likely that small increases in mesh size will be made over a period of years from the present mesh size of 70 mm to a maximum of 90 mm. A number of mesh-size changes will be made, and with them, a number of predictions of increased catch. If the predictions are fulfilled, chances of the increase being really due to recruitment changes will be very low within the North Sea area.

Natural Changes

Of much more interest is the real and possibly measurable effect of environmental changes on the theoretical structure which has been discussed. The parameters of natural mortality and growth express the effect of the environment on the stock in its widest sense. Figure 48 shows the relationship between log K (growth rate) and log temperature (4.5° C–12.0° C) for a set of cod stocks in the North Atlantic (Taylor,

1958). In other words, growth rate is inversely related to temperature. If all the cod stocks were interchangeable and mixed into one large one ranging from Cape Hatteras to Novaya Zemlya, the yield curve modified by the effects of temperature would be profoundly different. For any one of the cod stocks in the North Atlantic, however, separate estimates of K can be made, the range of each of which is small when compared with that given in Figure 48. But Taylor's point is a real one. Differences in K between different cod stocks, as, for example, between Cape Hatteras and Labrador, are differences generated by the environment and are perhaps mediated by temperature directly.

The growth rate of the North Sea herring has changed considerably in recent years. Values of K and W_∞ in the following list are indicative of growth parameters in some recent year classes for the Downs stock of the North Sea herring (Cushing and Bridger, 1966):

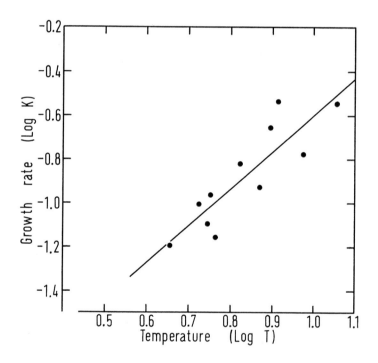

Figure 48. Relationship between log K and log temperature for a number of cod stocks of the North Atlantic. Adapted from Taylor, 1958.

	1932	*1943*	*1947*	*1950*	*1953*
K	0.354	0.308	0.402	0.462	0.569
W_∞	196.5	214.9	224.0	224.2	198.0

Between the observed values of K and W_∞, there is no relationship. There should be an inverse relation between K and W_∞ within the life of a fish, but it need not appear between year classes. It appears that W_∞ has increased sharply, but that K has not fallen to the extent that might have been expected.

Figure 42 (*bottom*) shows the yield curves of herring calculated for the five year classes, with K and W_∞ being used as observed in the growth-parameter list immediately above. At a fair value of F, Y_w/R' can change by as much as 20 per cent due to observed changes in growth parameters. It is likely that such growth changes (in addition to changes in recruitment) have had marked effects on the yields of herring in the North Sea. Growth changes have even tended to mask the changes due to fishing.

As will be observed in Chapter 7, the ratios M/K and L_m/L_∞ (where L_m is the length at first reaching maturity) between species in the same family tend to be constant. Within the same species or within a stock, however, there might be a certain variability, as shown in the above growth-parameter list. But the environment could have an unexpected component. Imagine an astronomical increase of a predator in the North Sea, all of which fed on herring. As a consequence, natural mortality of the North Sea herring would increase by many times. Obviously, such an effect would bear no immediate relationship to the growth parameters. There is also a "physiological" component of "natural" mortality, as, for example, in Bodenheimer's (1938) flies, which lived shorter lives under conditions of greater activity. In the sea, this situation could not be common; most "natural" deaths must be a form of predation because dead fish are so rarely caught. Some independent variance in predation would be an essential component to any balance between predators and prey. It is possible that the growth processes summarized by the two growth constants vary independently to some degree.

Summary

The procedures described in this chapter can be used to determine the exploitation proper to any stock of fish. They are in use by the international commissions working in the North Atlantic and the North

Pacific. There are three lines of development along which assessments of fish stocks might be improved. The first is by making the best use of the maximum sustainable yield in economic terms. This objective is obviously difficult to attain internationally, but a fishery exploited by one nation might well benefit from such analysis. The second is by assessing fully the effect of the environment on a fish stock through its vital parameters, R, M, K, and W_∞. Catches can be affected by secular trends in growth and recruitment, and the international assessments should eventually take such trends into account. The third is by estimating more fully the dependence of recruitment on parent stock. The present dogma that recruitment is independent of stock through its fishable range has outlined its usefulness and might even be dangerous. The scientific problem is explored in Chapter 8.

7 | Growth Problems and Fisheries Research

THREE aspects of growth, apparently quite disconnected from each other, are described in this chapter. The first is a comparative study, in groups of fish species, of the constants in the von Bertalanffy (1934) growth equation. The second aspect is the experimental analysis of growth, and the third is the effect of growth changes in the North Sea herring fisheries.

Both enlighten the comparative study of growth constants, which are essential to the useful application of the results of fisheries research. There is a large mass of data in the study of many fish populations, and a comparison leads to some broad generalizations: that bigger fish tend to live longer, that short-lived fish tend to grow quickly, and that a fish tends to mature according to a fixed proportion of its asymptotic weight. The second aspect of growth, its experimental analysis in terms of behavior, is based on the close observation of one fish and the food it takes in rather short time periods. Food intake depends on the quantity of food in the water, its patchiness, and on the sizes of individual food organisms. The third aspect, the study of growth in the North Sea herring fisheries, is concerned with the efficiency of feeding, the changes in density of the dominant food organism, and the consequences of these changes in the fisheries.

In his study of the growth of animals in general, including fish, Medawar (1945) clearly formulated the specific growth rate, γ, as it decreases with age:

$$\gamma = \frac{1}{t_1 - t_o} \log_e \frac{W_1}{W_o},$$ (49)

where W_0 is weight at t_0, and

W_1 is weight at t_1.

The generalization can be expressed in a number of growth equations (see Brody, 1945). Von Bertalanffy's equation (1934) has been used in fisheries dynamics because the growth constants are incorporated quite easily into the yield equations. Fish growth differs from mammalian growth in that the specific growth rate does not decrease so sharply with age (Bidder, 1925).

The conversion of food into weight by fish may be expressed in terms of percentage as weight in growth divided by weight in food. Under conditions of much available food and a water temperature of 11.5° C, the conversion efficiency of brown trout (*Salmo trutta* Linnaeus) ranges from 10.5 per cent to 18.7 per cent (Brown, 1946*a*, 1946*b*); this estimate includes the effect of physical and physiological maintenance. Another way of estimating metabolism is by measuring oxygen consumption (Winberg, 1956). Table 6 summarizes some calculations that Winberg has made from an extensive number of weight measurements and measurements of oxygen consumption.

In fisheries research, the problem is to link the growth constants found to the physiological bases, as briefly described, to the behavioral and ecological factors, as observed. In this way the natural history of a fish population can acquire quantitative expression.

Comparative Study of Growth Constants and Natural Mortality

A lake sturgeon (*Acipenser fulvescens* Rafinesque) has been found with 151 rings on its scales, but about 45 years would be a normal old age for this species (Probst and Cooper, 1954). A freshwater atherinid, *Labidesthes sicculus* (Cope), spawns at the age of one year and dies two or three months later (Hubbs, 1921). A North Sea herring lives from 10 to 14 years (Hodgson, 1925), but a Norwegian herring lives to the age of 23 (Lea, 1930). The origin of such differences is evolutionary and

Table 6.—Percentage of weight in daily calculated ration and weight increase for fish of various sizes (after Winberg, 1956)

Wt of fish in g wet wt	Daily ration as per cent of wt	Daily weight gain as per cent of wt
0.001	89.5–37.6	43.0–1.50
0.1	35.4–14.9	17.0–0.59
10.0	14.4– 6.0	6.9–0.24
1000.0	5.6– 2.4	2.7–0.09

inaccessible, but the differences in themselves are instructive. Differences such as these may be studied by comparing the growth constants, K and W_∞ from the von Bertalanffy growth equation and the natural mortality coefficient, M, throughout a range of fish groups.

Figure 49 shows the relationship between T_{max}, the oldest recorded age, and L_∞, the asymptotic length, for the Clupeoidei, Gadiformes, Pleuronectoidei, and Salmonoidei (Beverton and Holt, 1959). The obvious interpretation is that bigger fish live longer. This is not necessarily so, because the big and heavy tunas do not appear to live very long (Tiews, 1963). The interesting point is really in the difference between groups. The L_∞ at a T_{max} of 20 years is as follows: Clupeoidei, 40 cm; Pleuronectoidei, 60 cm; Salmonoidei, 80 cm; and Gadiformes, 135 cm. In other words, cod-like fishes are bigger for their age than the herring-like fish.

For the same four groups, there is a relationship between M, the coefficient of natural mortality, and K, the rate at which growth to the asymptote decreases (Fig. 50; Beverton and Holt, 1959). The data are somewhat scattered, despite good sampling, but in general a fish with a high growth rate dies young. When Figure 49 (which gives the relationship between T_{max} and L_∞) and Figure 50 are compared, T_{max} is obviously inversely related to K. So the relationship between M and K should not be unexpected. The practical value of such a relationship is to set reasonable values of M in models, given K, and K can be easily measured. The difference between groups is established by classifying K at $M = 1.0$: Clupeoidei, 0.9; Pleuronectoidei, 1.0; Salmonoidei, 0.6; and Gadiformes, 0.45. In other words, the herring-like fish grow to their maximum size much more quickly in "physiological age" than the cod-like fish.

Beverton (1963) has established a relationship between L_m, the length at first reaching maturity and L_∞ for a number of clupeid families. The bigger the fish is, the bigger it is at first reaching maturity. In other words, for a given family, L_m/L_∞ is a constant ratio. Between many clupeid families, the two ratios, M/K and L_m/L_∞, tend to be inversely related. This could really be a function of the inverse relationship between K and L_∞. It might be that when the reproductive load is high ($L_m/L_\infty = 0.8$–0.9), the fraction M/K tends to be low.

There is a sense in which the statement of these relationships between growth parameters is obvious, e.g., bigger fish often live longer. But there are many uses for the ratios M/K and L_m/L_∞, because the differences between groups are so easily described. Such differences can be formulated numerically and can be related to the absolute magnitudes of the coefficients themselves. The magnitude of M is presumably the

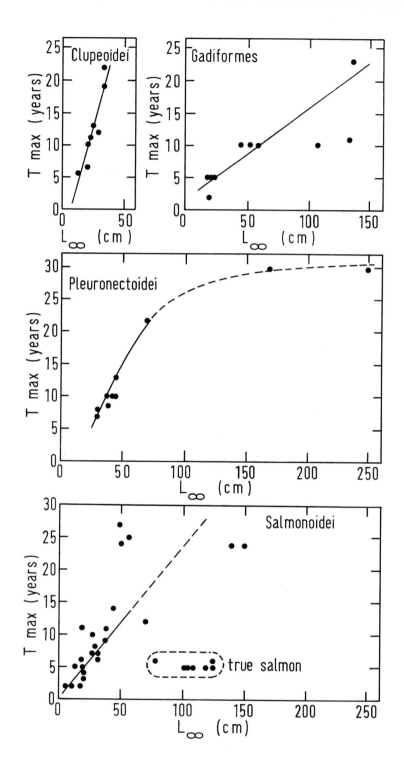

sum of predations for little fish; for predators it is more nearly a "natural" mortality in a physiological sense, but is dependent on their place in the food chain. Variations in L_∞ may be correlated with variations in feeding efficiency. When such constants have been given a fuller physiological and ecological meaning, these ratios will more completely and fully describe differences in growth between fish groups.

Experimental Ecology of Feeding

This section is a summary of some of the work of Ivlev (1961). He has worked on freshwater fish kept in small tanks for rather short time

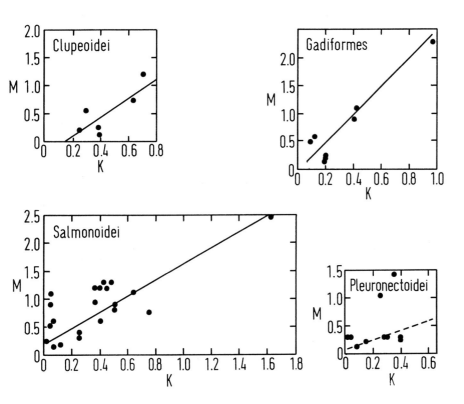

Figure 49 (facing). The relationship between the oldest recorded age, T_{max}, and the asymptotic length, L_∞, for the Clupeoidei, Gadiformes, Pleuronectoidei, and Salmonoidei. Adapted from Beverton and Holt, 1959.

Figure 50. The relationship between natural mortality, M, and the rate at which fish grow to their asymptotic length, K, for the Clupeoidei, Gadiformes, Pleuronectoidei, and Salmonoidei. Adapted from Beverton and Holt, 1959.

periods. The quantity of food eaten was estimated in one of three ways: (1) by calculating the quantity left over from the quantity given; (2) by estimating the quantity eaten in the presence of an observer; and (3) from gut contents, the fish having been starved for 18–20 hours before each experiment. The experiment lasted $1\frac{1}{2}$–2 hours, after which the fish were killed. Much of his work was analyzed using the following equation:

$$\frac{dr}{dp} = \kappa(\omega - r), \tag{50}$$

where r is the daily ration, or quantity eaten per day,
    ω is the maximum ration,
    p is the concentration of food, and
    κ is the feeding coefficient.

$$\therefore r = \omega(1 - e^{-\kappa p}). \tag{51}$$

Figure 51 shows the effect of concentration, p, on the daily ration, r. The three lines on the graph represent carp (*Cyprinus carpio* Linnaeus) feeding on the roe of bream (*Abramis brama* Linnaeus), roach (*Leuciscus rutilus* Fleming) feeding on chironomid larvae, and bleak (*Alburnus alburnus* Linnaeus) feeding on *Daphnia*. In each situation the daily ration depends on the concentration in a negatively exponential way. The exponent, like that in the von Bertalanffy (1934) growth equation, is the rate at which the maximum ration is reached in relation to concentration, and it decreases as the maximum ration is approached.

The effect of patchiness (Fig. 52) is expressed by means of an index of aggregation:

$$\varsigma = \sqrt{\Sigma\left(\frac{\nu^2}{\bar{p}}\right)}, \tag{52}$$

where ς is the index of aggregation,
    ν is the deviation in density from the mean of a series in space, and
    $\bar{p}$ is the mean food density.
Let

$$\frac{dr}{dp} = \chi(\omega - r), \tag{53}$$

where χ is the concentration coefficient.

$$\therefore r = \omega(1 - e^{-\chi p}), \tag{54}$$

Figure 52 shows the daily ration as a percentage of the maximum ration plotted against ζ, the index of aggregation. In other words, as the food at a constant mean density becomes more patchy, so the daily ration increases. The relation is expressed by

$$r = \theta + (\omega - p)(1 - e^{-x\zeta}) , \qquad (55)$$

where θ is the daily ration, at zero aggregation, as a percentage of the maximum ration.

The curves are drawn to the data in Figure 52.

When Ivlev (1961) combined the two sets of experiments, he found that the daily ration depended partly on the concentration of the prey and partly on its patchiness. He has shown that when carp were feeding on benthos in the Volga, patchiness of food was more important than its density in governing the magnitude of the daily ration (as a percentage of the maximum, ω). Patchiness is, of course, the rule in the sea, largely because of variations in reproduction and predation in space and time. It is useful in promoting efficient feeding, since the distance

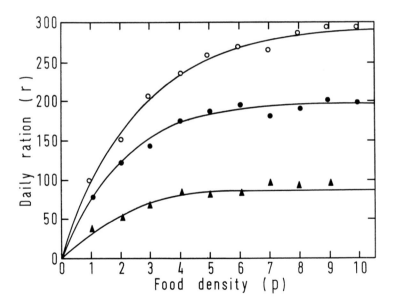

Figure 51. The effect of concentration of food, p, in mg/cm² on the daily ration, r, in mg for carp feeding on bream roe (open circles), roach feeding on chironomid larvae (closed circles), and bleak feeding on *Daphnia* (triangles). Adapted from Ivlev, 1961.

between patches may be considerably less than the summed distance between the number of evenly distributed individuals.

There is an analogy here with shoaling fish, for the chance of encounter by a predator is inversely proportional to the number of fish in the shoal. Such a situation involves more than mere patchiness, which supposes a continuum between groups. Presumably the patchily distributed planktonic prey have not evolved a response to predation as have the analogous shoals of plankton-feeding fish—fish being able to communicate with each other and to form shoals.

Ivlev (1961) has also made a study of food selection. He uses an index of selection,

$$\eta = \frac{u_i - v_j}{u_i + v_j}, \tag{56}$$

where u is the percentage of an ingredient, i, of food in the gut,

v is the percentage of an ingredient, j, of food in the water.

When η is positive, the predator selects the prey. When it is negative,

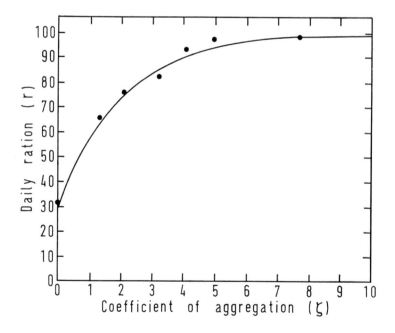

Figure 52. The daily ration, r, as a percentage of a maximum ration, θ, plotted on the index of aggregation, ζ. In other words, the daily ration increases with patchiness. Adapted from Ivlev, 1961.

it discriminates against the prey. In one experiment, Ivlev offered six successive rations comprising five different food items—chironomids, amphipods, an inert food, isopods, and mollusks, each food being offered in the order given. The predator was a carp, and it obviously liked the chironomids best, even though they were not selected immediately. In another experiment, bleak were given five successive rations of four different food items—*Daphnia*, *Bosmina* (a water flea), *Diaptomus*, and *Cypris* larvae. In contrast to the carp's delayed selectivity, the bleak not only preferred *Daphnia* but liked them instantly. In these two patterns of feeding behavior, carp discriminated as hunger decreased, and bleak discriminated immediately.

From the relationship between selection index and weight of prey (Fig. 53), the simple conclusion is that there is an optimum size of prey for each predator (Ivlev, 1961). Curves are sometimes symmetrical and are sometimes skewed. It is possible that the skewness is a function of the speed of the prey. Indeed, Figure 53 is the sort of picture that might be expected if the largest prey had some capacity to escape the predator. By dividing the optimum weight of prey by the weight of the predator, Ivlev established rapacity indices for some of his experimental animals: bleak, 0.00038; bream, 0.0019; carp, 0.13; perch (*Perca fluviatilis* Linnaeus), 0.18; pike (*Esox lucius* Linnaeus), 0.32; and a water beetle of the genus *Macrodytes*, 0.65. Presumably a very active and rapacious fish can afford to be idle for considerable periods, whereas a less active fish has to maintain its feeding more continuously.

From those of Ivlev's experiments that have been reported above, the following conclusions can be drawn: (1) that the daily ration depends on concentration and on patchiness; (2) that plankton-eaters and benthos-eaters exhibit different patterns of behavior in their food selection; (3) that there is an optimum size of prey for each predator.

The fact that there is an optimum size of prey for each predator supposes that there is a spread in prey size, which must correspond to a spread in the growth constants of a fish population. It is likely that the constants will vary in their means, depending first on food concentration and secondly on its patchiness. Hence, the growth constants of a population must vary both randomly and systematically. The pronounced differences in dynamic constants among fish groups, as described in the previous section, probably originated in the small behavioral differences between plankton-eaters and benthos-eaters.

Description of Growth of the North Sea Herring

Hardy et al. (1936) have shown that catches of herring are sometimes greater when associated with high catches of *Calanus* (Fig. 5). In

another description of the same process (Cushing, 1952), patches of
pelagic fish were recorded by echo survey from research ships. Patches
of *Calanus*, the preferred food of the herring, were located by the same
research ships using plankton nets. Since echo patches and *Calanus*
patches coincided, there is every indication that pelagic fish, probably
herring, aggregate to the patches of *Calanus*.

Savage (1937) examined the gut contents from 100 North Sea herring
in each fortnight from May through September for five years. In four
years out of the five, *Calanus* predominated by weight in the guts of the
herring. In tank experiments, Battle (1935) observed the digestion rate
of herring at different water temperatures. With Battle's information,
the results of Savage's experiments on the weight and number of individual *Calanus* found in the gut can be converted into quantities
consumed per day. The number of individuals in the gut each day
represents the number of successful attacks made, and the daily weight
in the gut is a measure of the total effectiveness of feeding. Figure 54

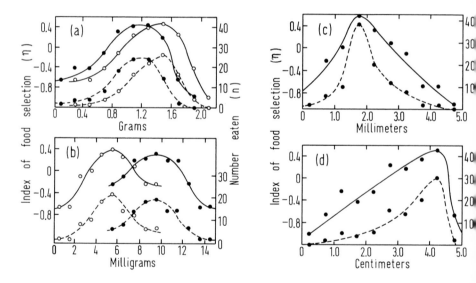

Figure 53. Relationship between the food selection index (solid line) and size of the pr
as a percentage distribution in weight or length of the number eaten (dashed line). There is
optimum size of prey for each predator. The four parts of the figure represent: (*a*) pike f
on roach (open circles), perch fed on roach (closed circles); (*b*) carp fed on chironomid larv
(open circles), bream fed on amphipods (closed circles); (*c*) bleak fed on water fleas; and
larvae of a water beetle (*Macrodytes circumflexus*) fed on young roach. Adapted from Ivl
1961.

shows the relationship between the number of attacks made daily (averaged for fortnightly periods) and the weight of food in the gut for each of the five years (Cushing, 1964a). The curves could well be of the type formulated by Ivlev (1961) in his Equation (51).

From each of the curves in Figure 54 it is possible to obtain a measure of efficiency from the number of attacks made per ml of food in the gut. The quantity of food eaten per encounter from each of the five years can be used to plot efficiency on weight in the gut or on the maximum number of *Calanus* in the gut (Fig. 55; Cushing, 1964a). The greatest weight in the gut is found at a middle efficiency—about 1,000 successful attacks per ml of food in the gut. The weight of food varies as the product of the sizes of the prey and the numbers of prey. As size varies inversely with density in numbers, there must be an optimum size of prey for each predator, as Ivlev concluded from his experiments. As *Calanus* is the dominant food organism of the herring, it must be the largest prey for its density in numbers per unit volume searched by the fish.

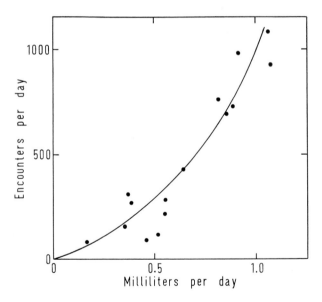

Figure 54. Number of attacks or encounters made daily (averaged for fortnightly periods) by herring, plotted on the weight of food in the gut, in the year 1931. Adapted from Cushing, 1964a after data in Savage, 1937.

Changes in growth in herring populations for long periods of time are conveniently expressed in length. In Figure 56, the mean lengths of each age group (3–9) of herring in the East Anglian fishery are shown for the periods 1932–39 and 1946–59 (Cushing, 1960). The mean length of the stock, drawn as a bolder line, declines sharply in later years as older fish disappear from the fishery (Fig. 9). The notable point is the large increment in lengths of three-year-olds in 1949–50 and that of four-year-olds in 1950–51.

The correlation between periods of herring growth and a high density of *Calanus* has been studied by Burd and Cushing (1962), who averaged

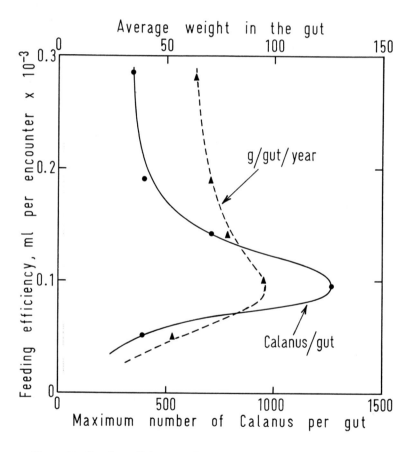

Figure 55. Grazing efficiency of herring (as the quantity of food eaten per encounter) plotted on weight in gut or on maximum number of *Calanus* in the gut; based on five years' data. Adapted from Cushing, 1964a, after data in Savage, 1937.

the number of *Calanus* estimated to be in the area between the English
coast and the Dogger Bank from April to September in the periods
1933–38 and 1946–58. The samples were taken near the area in which
the immature herring live. Very generally, the period of greater growth
coincided with the period of high *Calanus* density in the early 1950's.
Colebrook (1963), analyzing the distribution of *Calanus* by statistical
rectangles in the southern North Sea, found that the best correlation
between herring growth and *Calanus* was obtained by using *Calanus*
samples from the herring nursery ground east of the Dogger Bank. It
must be pointed out that the herring were growing steadily, if rather
slowly, during the 1930's when the density of *Calanus* was low.

There is a close relationship between the mean length of the three-
year-old herring at East Anglia and the density of *Calanus* in the sea
averaged for the three years of the fishes' growth (Fig. 57). It implies

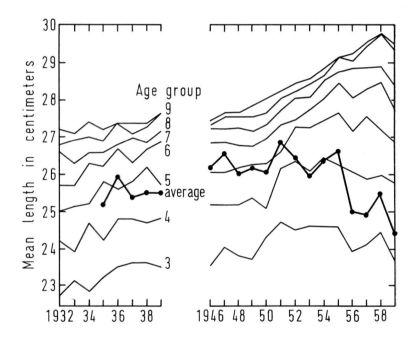

Figure 56. Mean lengths, in cm, of herring of age groups 3–9 in the East
Anglian fishery in 1932–39 and 1946–59. The mean length is shown as a
bold line; it decreased sharply after 1954, as the older age groups vanished
from the fishery. There were increments in length of three-year-old fish
between 1949 and 1950, and of four-year-old fish between 1950 and 1951.
Adapted from Cushing, 1960.

that the growth of young herring around the Dogger Bank is dependent upon the density of *Calanus* in the sea there.

The proportion of recruits at a given age in the herring depends on the length for age, so any dependence of length on *Calanus* density will have an effect on the recruitment pattern. Figure 58 shows the percentage of recruits for three-, four-, and five-year-old fish in the East Anglian fishery in 1924–37 and 1946–54. There were two changes in the recruitment pattern, first in 1925–28 and secondly in 1950–52. In the first pattern change, the predominantly five-year-old recruitment gave way to four-year-old recruitment, and in the second, predominantly four-year-old recruitment gave way to predominantly three-year-old recruitment. The changes in the age distribution that took place in 1950–52 in the East Anglian herring fishery were changes in recruitment linked to growth changes. The change in recruitment pattern to the Buchan spawning fishery is similar to that picturing the relevant age distribution in catch per effort in the East Anglian fishery (Fig. 9). Not only did the fish recruit at a younger age to the Buchan fishery, but the spawning stock's quantity of recruitment increased sharply in

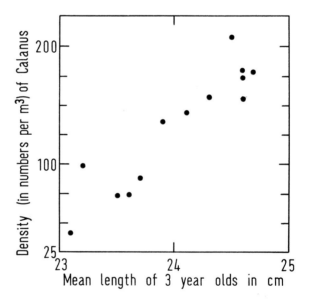

Figure 57. Relationship between the mean length of three-year-old herring at East Anglia and the density of *Calanus*, averaged for the three years of growth. Adapted from Burd and Cushing, 1962.

1952 and in subsequent years (Burd and Cushing, 1962). It is possible that the change in recruitment to the Buchan spawning fishery resulted from the same events that altered the pattern of recruitment to the East Anglian fishery.

The patterns of migration in recruiting fish are hard to disentangle. From the nursery ground east of the Dogger Bank, the herring probably move northeastward in autumn to join the northern stocks, and southwestward in spring to join the southern stocks. The southern group moves into the fishery off North Shields on the northeastern English coast in early summer. Figure 59 gives the percentage of herring at maturity stage I (virgins) (Hjort, 1910) in the fishery off North Shields for the years 1952–58 (Burd, in Burd and Cushing, 1962). The 50 per cent point on the ogive is at about 21 cm. Burd and Cushing (1962) have found that the mean age of 21-cm fish decreases during the summer. As the season proceeds, the herring in these length groups become younger, i.e., from three to two years of age.

The length of 21 cm has been called the critical length, the length at which herring start to mature and recruit to the adult fisheries (Burd and Cushing, 1962). If growth is rapid, the critical length is reached sooner; if slow, it is reached later. Throughout all the recruitment changes (as applied to the East Anglian herring), it is possible that the critical length remains the same (the lengths of stage I fish off North Shields in the 1920's [Hodgson, 1925] are the same as those in the 1950's [Burd and Cushing, 1962]). If critical length is constant, the length at first maturity, L_m, is likely to remain the same. Since L_∞ is known to increase (see above), then L_m/L_∞ may possibly vary within a stock such as that of the East Anglian herring.

The dependence of herring growth on *Calanus* density has had far-

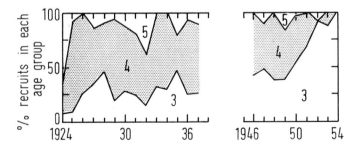

Figure 58. Percentage of recruits at three, four, and five years of age in the East Anglian herring fishery in 1924–37 and 1946–54. Adapted from Cushing and Burd, 1957.

reaching effects on the North Sea herring fisheries. The recruitment pattern has changed and it is possible, though not yet demonstrated, that the Bløden fishery for immature herring and the Sandettié fishery

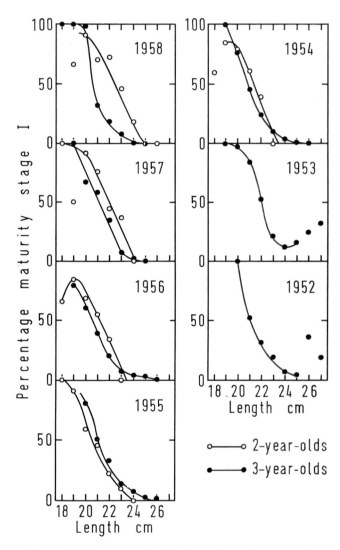

Figure 59. Percentage distributions of maturing virgin herring at North Shields, on the northeastern English coast, in Hjort maturity stage I. In general, the 50 per cent point is at 21 cm or 22 cm, whether the fish are two or three years old. This length has been termed the "critical length." Adapted from Burd and Cushing, 1962.

for adult herring owe their origin (but not their continued existence) to this change. The recruitment change in the northern North Sea has led to an increase in stock of about three times. Another consequence, as shown in Chapter 5, has been an increase of about 20 per cent in the yield of herring for a given fairly substantial fishing intensity. As pointed out in Chapter 6, the changes due to fishing have been masked by the growth changes. By whatever standard, the changes resulting from changes in *Calanus* density are profound ones. The origin of the *Calanus* changes is at the present time unknown.

Summary

Growth has been examined in three ways—by comparing the growth constants in a range of groups, by using experimental ecology, and by studying the growth history of herring in the North Sea. The comparison of growth parameters has shown that the ratios M/K and L_m/L_∞ appear to be constant within groups. The first ratio expresses the fact that fish dying young grow quickly, and vice versa; the second ratio expresses the character of the reproductive load. In the North Sea herring, the reproductive load appears to be safeguarded by the critical length. Fish do not start to mature until they have reached it, and it appears to remain constant despite changes in L_∞. Considerable changes have taken place in the growth of the herring. Stock changes have occurred which are associated with changes in the density of *Calanus*, the preferred food in the sea. It is possible that the size of *Calanus* is the optimum one required by herring. Such a relationship was shown experimentally by Ivlev for a number of fishes; he also showed that the daily ration depended on the food's concentration and patchiness. Hence if the preferred food, or food of the optimum size, became more abundant, the herring would be expected to grow more quickly and to mature earlier in their lives.

In such a context, growth is a complex phenomenon. The basic growth study is the experimental one, illuminating the natural history and the nature of the growth constants. Perhaps the most unknown aspect of the study is that of the reproductive load. A comparative study of growth constants may indicate that the reproductive load of pelagic fish is much greater than that of demersal fish. Such factors must be of the magnitude of K, which controls the shape of the growth curve. If the function of the critical length is to safeguard the reproductive load, it is an essential feature in the natural history of the herring. It is presumably a subject which is amenable to the form of experimental treatment pioneered by Ivlev.

8 | Stock and Recruitment

WHEN fishermen think of overfishing, they believe that the run of smaller fish is due to a reduction of stock to a level at which young are no longer produced in sufficient numbers to maintain the stock. As shown in Chapter 6, reduction in the stock of many demersal fish leads to a sharp reduction in the mean weight of the stock, because the little fish are caught before they have had a chance to grow.

Under such conditions, the number of recruits to a stock at a low level can remain as high as at a high stock level. However, many of the catastrophic failures of fisheries have been true failures in recruitment. Such was the failure of the Plymouth herring in the early 1930's, perhaps due to competition with pilchards (Cushing, 1961). Recruitment to the California sardine stock failed in the late 1940's (Marr, 1960), and subsequently the species has probably been replaced by the anchovy (*Engraulis mordax* Girard) (Ahlstrom, 1966). So the fishermen's question remains, Can recruitment fail because the stock has become thinned through fishing? No catastrophic failure of recruitment to a fish stock has been decisively attributed to fishing, although the effect of fishing on the recruitment to some Pacific salmon stocks is perhaps noticeable (Rounsefell, 1958). There are two reasons why the fishermen's question has not been properly answered. The first is that there is very often no relation between parent stock and subsequent recruitment at those levels of stock which support fisheries. The second reason is that the failure of recruitment might result from a single event never to be repeated in quite the same frame of circumstances.

Changes in Catch in Some Fish Stocks

The failure of recruitment to the California sardine stock is sometimes attributed to fishing and sometimes to natural causes (Clark and

Marr, 1956, discuss both aspects). Between 1932 and 1950 there was a
clear dependence of stock density on fishing effort (Schaefer, 1954),
but after 1950 a new relationship was established (Marr, 1960), imply-
ing no dependence of stock density on fishing effort (Fig. 60). The con-
troversy in California has revolved around the question whether the
failure in recruitment in 1951 was generated by the stock having been
fished until that date, or whether a purely natural change in recruitment took place then. Murphy (1966) has contrasted the reproductive
conditions in the stock (in Ricker's terms of P_r and P_m; see below) when
fishing was taking place with conditions when the only cause of mortality was natural death. He suggests that the reproductive capacity
of the stock was reduced by fishing. There was a single event, the complete failure of recruitment with the 1949 year class, on which to make
a judgment and the change might have been irreversible, especially if
a competitive replacement of sardine by anchovy took place (Marr,
1960).

Some of the dramatic changes in catch are shown in Figure 61. Over
a period of half a century, catches of the Japanese sardine (*Sardinops*

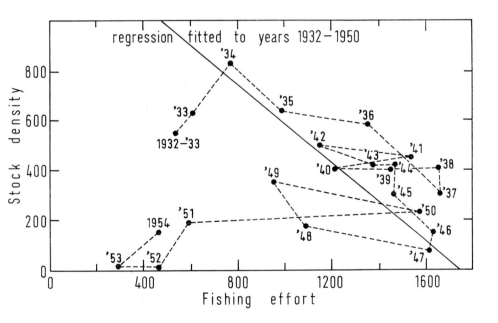

Figure 60. The relationship of stock density on fishing effort for the California sardine from
1932 to 1954; the line was fitted to the data for the years 1932–50. After 1950, a quite different relationship was established. Adapted from Marr, 1960.

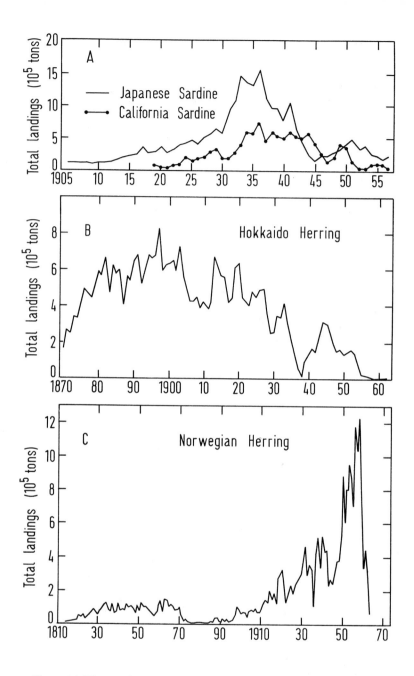

Figure 61. The catches over long periods of time for: (*A*) the Japanese sardine and the California sardine; adapted from Yamanaka, 1960; (*B*) the Hokkaido (or Sakhalin) herring; adapted from Motoda and Hirano, 1963; and (*C*) the Norwegian herring; adapted from Devold, 1963.

melanosticta [Temminck and Schlegel]) varied by a factor of fifteen, and changes in catches of the California sardine were of the order of one hundred times (Yamanaka, 1960). Catches of the Hokkaido herring (*Clupea pallasi* Cuvier and Valenciennes) (Motoda and Hirano, 1963) and of the Norwegian herring (Devold, 1963) fluctuated with equal sharpness. Changes of great magnitude are shown over long periods. Those of the Norwegian herring stock have fluctuated for centuries, as recorded in the Icelandic sagas (Devold, 1963). Even during the 1950's, fishing mortality represented a minor proportion of total mortality, as shown from the extensive tagging results (Gulland, 1955*b*). Hence, the great fluctuations of the Norwegian herring are possibly due to natural causes. There is not enough evidence to decide between fishing and natural causes for the Japanese sardine or the Hokkaido herring stocks. The four stocks, the fluctuations of which are shown in Figure 61, are herring-like fishes, and are therefore pelagic. The figure documents the range of fluctuation, which is known well to the fishermen. Traditionally, fishermen expect the herring-like fishes to appear and disappear. The causes of the violent variation are quite unknown save that they are basically changes in the magnitude of recruitment.

Beverton (1962) has calculated the trends in catches for certain North Sea stocks of demersal fish in a fairly long time series (Fig. 62). The North Sea cod catches have remained steady for 51 years. Turbot and plaice catches have increased slightly. Sole catches, however, have increased by ten times, and the haddock catches have fallen by an appreciable amount. The sudden and dramatic changes among some species of pelagic fish are contrasted with the slow changes in certain species of demersal fish for about half a century. It is not necessarily a contrast between all pelagic and demersal stocks, but it does seem to be true that pelagic fish can suffer dramatic changes in recruitment. There are no differences in larval habit or spawning behavior between the two groups of fish. The only difference is really one in growth. The pelagic fish grow quickly and demersal fish grow slowly. Pelagic fish tend to be small and demersal ones tend to be large.

The Nature of the Problem

The coefficient of variation of recruitment to the East Anglian herring stock is 250 per cent, and that for the arctic cod stock is perhaps from two to four times greater (Garrod, 1967). The arctic cod lays 4 million eggs, from which only two fish survive long enough to become adults. The implication is that there is a very fine adjustment of mortality, high stock numbers yielding the same level of recruitment as low stock. In the southern North Sea plaice, there is no relationship between stock and recruitment in all of the available data (Beverton, 1962). The lack of correlation extends over a period of 26 years. Figure 63 shows the index of survival (recruitment as a proportion of the stock) related to the weight of the plaice stock (Beverton, 1962). The

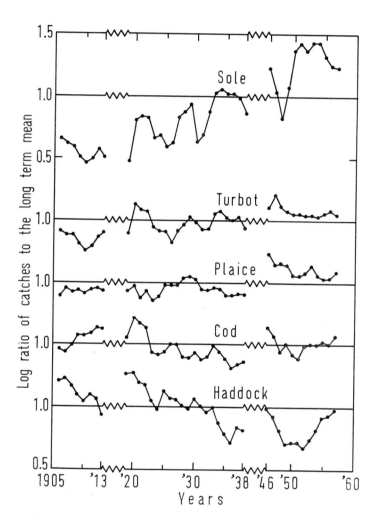

Figure 62. The logarithmic ratio of catches to the long-term mean (1906–57) of certain demersal species in the North Sea; the logarithmic ratio is used only to reduce the scale. Adapted from Beverton, 1962.

ratio of maximum to minimum is about 20 to 1 for the survival-rate
index for a range of about 10 to 1 in the total adult population weight.
If survival is higher at low stock levels, a density-dependent mortality
operates between hatching and recruitment. Consequently the stock
has a mechanism allowing it to recover from setback or even from
disaster; such a mechanism is called "compensatory." Another form
of compensation is shown in the inverse relationship between the
stock of pilchards in the western Channel and subsequent recruitment
(Cushing, 1961). This stock is virtually unfished and is more abundant
than the plaice stock of the southern North Sea. This fact suggests
perhaps another form of compensatory expression—where density-
dependent mortality among young fish is high enough at high stock
levels to reduce the total recruitment. The problem of stock and recruitment is a difficult one because of the nature of this compensatory
mechanism. But it is of very great importance, because it is perhaps
at the root of the great fluctuations in the fisheries. Hence, its nature
should be examined in some detail.

Hjort (1926) has suggested that fluctuations in year classes are the
result of a "critical period" in larval life—a critical period being one of
high mortality, due to starvation when the yolk is exhausted. There is

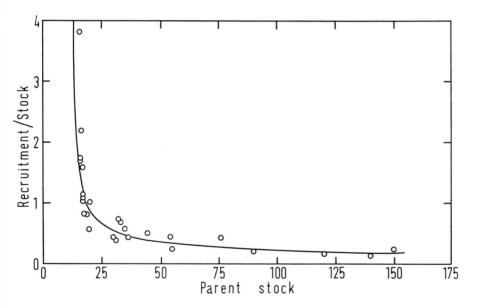

Figure 63. Index of recruit survival (or ratio of recruitment to parent stock) at different
stock levels in weight of plaice in the southern North Sea. Adapted from Beverton, 1962.

not much evidence that there is such a critical period. The larvae are
sampled by plankton nets, and the larger ones may escape. Rarely has
larval mortality been separated from the two loss rates due to escape
from the nets and to diffusion of larvae from the spawning center. Marr
(1956) has published a larval survival curve for the Atlantic mackerel
(*Scomber scombrus* Linnaeus) (Fig. 64) derived by Ahlstrom and Nair
using Sette's information. There is no difference in Sette's original data
between the day and night catches of larvae, so the larvae did not escape the net in the daytime; therefore it is likely that this curve represents both mortality and diffusion. Egg mortality is less than the early
larval mortality. Later, at the time of metamorphosis, there is a step-
like increase in mortality, which may be due to an increase in the escape

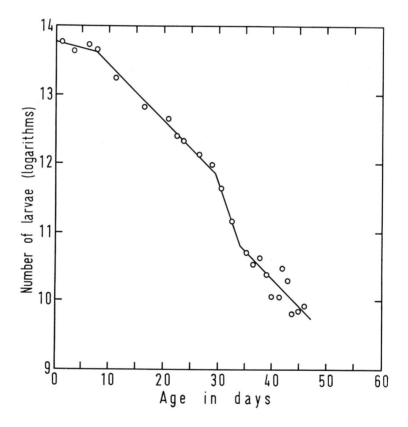

Figure 64. The larval mortality of the Atlantic mackerel. Adapted from
Marr, 1956, after curve derived by Ahlstrom and Nair, using Sette's data.

of larvae from the nets. In a laboratory study, Farris (1960) found that the high mortality of larval sardines starts well before the yolk is exhausted, and Strasburg (1959) and Marr (1956) have recorded catches of dead larvae of sardines and other species in plankton nets. There is no evidence, in the studies cited, of Hjort's critical period at the time of yolk exhaustion, although there is some evidence that mortality increases significantly at the time of metamorphosis.

The best measure of larval mortality has been made by Pearcy (1962) in a study of the winter flounder (*Pseudopleuronectes americanus* [Walbaum]) in the estuary of the Mystic River in Connecticut. Because the sizes of larvae were shown to be the same by day and by night, it is unlikely that the bigger larvae were escaping from the nets during the daytime. There is a daily loss of about 30 per cent of the estuary volume to the sea, mostly near the surface. Since Pearcy found that about 85 per cent of the larvae remain close to the bottom, where the eggs are laid, the daily loss of larvae by translocation to the sea is about 3 per cent. The curve of larval survival with age is markedly concave, survival increasing sharply with age. From physical measurements, the translocation rate (percentage removed by seaward movement) was estimated as

$$\phi = 1 - (1 - m)^\psi , \tag{57}$$

where ϕ is the translocation rate,
    m is the proportion of larvae in the upper 2 m (where the main seaward translocation takes place), and
    ψ is the number of tidal cycles per day.
Since the percentage of both total loss and daily translocation are known, the remaining mortality can be attributed to natural mortality:

| Age | Percentage | | |
(in days)	Total loss	Translocation	Natural mortality
9–25	0.248	0.041	0.207
26–53	0.112	0.015	0.097

Thus, the natural mortality rate is five times the translocation rate in this case. As numbers became reduced, the natural mortality rate was halved in the second period as compared with the first. It is likely (but not shown) that this is a density-dependent mortality. Perhaps this period of high density-dependent mortality is the modern equivalent to Hjort's critical period.

Pearcy was also able to follow the steady decline in numbers during the course of survival of immature winter flounders up to the age of two years. The fish were sampled with a beam trawl and an otter trawl (Fig. 65). Pearcy suggests that the low numbers in January and February were due to the young fish burying themselves in the mud. It is not obvious that the two-year span of mortality is density dependent. Indeed, in the second year, the death rate is rather low.

Pearcy's technique of dividing total loss rate into translocation rate and natural mortality rate allowed him to specify the changes in natural mortality. If the critical period is one that is critical for the subsequent size of the year class, then it is possibly limited to a short period of high density dependence. If the nature of the dependence of mortality on density becomes understood, the nature of the compensatory mechanism will likely emerge.

The form of analysis needed may be seen from the material collected on larval and adolescent cod in the Danish Belt seas (Fig. 66). Yolk-sac larvae were collected with Petersen's young-fish trawl, and fish in age groups 0, I, and II were caught with an eel tog, which is a small trawl,

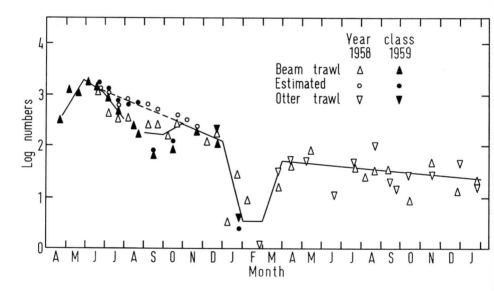

Figure 65. The survival of one- and two-year-old winter flounders. Numbers are expressed in logarithms per $10^5 m^2$. The otter trawl was used to catch the larger two-year-old fish, and the beam trawl to catch the smaller one-year-old fish. The "calculated" line takes into account some migrations, as estimated from seine-net catches. Adapted from Pearcy, 1962.

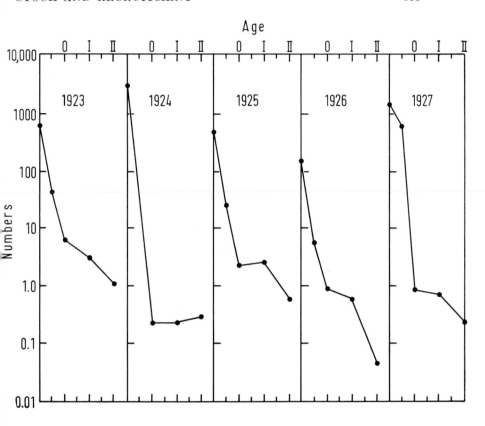

Figure 66. The larval and adolescent mortality of cod in age groups 0, I, and II in the Belt seas of eastern Denmark. Larvae were collected with a Petersen young-fish trawl, and fish from the 0, I, and II groups were caught with an eel tog, a form of small trawl. Data from Poulsen, 1930a, 1930b.

not very efficient but capable of indicating gross changes in abundance. The complete data were published by Poulsen (1930a, 1930b). If the initial number of eggs (as caught by Hensen net) is considered as stock and the final number of group II fish as number of recruits, then the intermediate mortalities might well describe the nature of compensation.

The nature of the problem relating parent stock to subsequent recruitment remains obscure. It is possible that the compensatory mechanism, ensuring high recruitment at low stock levels and low recruitment at high stock levels, is achieved by a density-dependent mortality. Such mortality is hard to separate from larval escape, diffusion of larvae, and death from other causes. Yet separation is possible by repeated sampling of the same stock in the sequence from hatching to recruitment.

The Comparative Study of Fecundity

Nikolsky (1953) has approached the problem in rather a different way. He has compared the fecundities of the same or closely related species in different regions. The nature of the regulatory mechanism probably depends on the existence of a density-dependent mortality. Other forms of mortality must occur. There must be differences in total loss, density dependent and density independent, which are reflected in the differences in fecundity between regions.

In Table 7, part (A) compares the fecundities of analogous species living in the Atlantic and in the Pacific, and part (B) those of pike and perch in the Aral and Caspian seas. From parts (A) and (B), it appears that larval and juvenile mortality tends to be greater in the Pacific

Table 7.—Fecundities of various species in thousands of eggs

Species or genus	Mean number of eggs per female	
(A)	ATLANTIC	PACIFIC
Mallotus	*M. villosus* Müller	*M. villosus*
	6.2–13.4	15.3–39.9
Limanda	*L. limanda* (Linnaeus)	*L. aspera* (Pallas)
	80.0–140.0	626.0–1133.0
Eleginus	*E. navaga* Pallas	*E. gracilis* (Tilesius)
	6.2–63.0	25.0–210.0
Hippoglossoides	*H. platessoides* (Fabricius)	*H. elassodon* Jordan & Gilbert
	240.0–370.0	211.0–241.0
Scomber	*S. scombrus* Linnaeus	*S. japonicus* Houttuyn
	350.0–450.0	400.0–850.0
Gadus	*G. morhua* Linnaeus	*G. macrocephalus* Tilesius
	570.0–930.0	170.0–600.0
Engraulis	*E. engrasicholus* (Linnaeus)	*E. japonicus* Schl.
	30.0	35.0
(B)	ARAL SEA	CASPIAN SEA
Pike, 30–40 cm	8.3	17.6
Perch, 16–20 cm	18.3	32.9
(C)	1940	1941	1946
Clupea pallasi Cuvier and			
Valenciennes, 25–26 cm	37.4	37.8	46.2
26–27 cm	40.6	43.1	49.4

than in the Atlantic (but not for *Hippoglossoides* or cod) and greater in the Caspian Sea than in the Aral Sea. The important point is that the difference is not restricted to one species. Again, the stocks are not larger in the Pacific than they are in the Atlantic. Perhaps the greater numbers of larval fish support a larger number of predators.

Nikolsky (1953) also suggests that fecundity can change from year to year. Part (C) of Table 7 gives the fecundities for three years of Sakhalin herring of the same lengths. The increase in fecundity for 1946 might at first give the impression that there is an advantage for a given stock size, but if the compensatory mechanism is operating, the apparent advantage would be nullified.

F. G. Martyshev (cited by Nikolsky, 1953) has shown that as carp grow older their eggs are larger:

Age	*3+*	*4+*	*8+*	*15+*	*17+*
Average egg diameter, in mm	1.26	1.39	1.71	1.52	1.64
Length of embryo on hatching, in mm	4.80	5.05	6.41	6.40	8.18

This suggests that the eggs of older fish are more viable than those of younger fish.

Bridger (1960) and Cushing and Bridger (1966) related larval abundance to the weight of the Downs herring stock for a number of year classes. The regression of larval abundance on stock size of older fish (five years of age or older) was linear and passed through the origin. That of larval abundance on total stock size (of younger as well as older fish) was linear, with a significant regression on the abscissa. When the two regressions were compared, the younger fish appeared to contribute no viable larvae. This state might be potentially dangerous to the stock.

The Theoretical Formulation of the Problem

Ricker (1954, 1958) has formulated the relationship between stock and recruitment in the following way:

$$\frac{R}{R_r} = \frac{P}{P_r} e^{(P_r - P)/P_m},\tag{58}$$

where R is the recruitment,
      P is the parent stock,
      P_r is the replacement size of stock,
      R_r is the number of recruits from P_r, and
      P_m is the stock producing maximum recruitment.

Then if recruitment and stock are expressed in the same units, R_r = P_r, so $R = Pe^{(Pr-P)/Pm}$. Let $a = P_r/P_m$; $W' = P/P_r$, then R/R_r = $W'e^{a(1-W')}$. This is a formal arrangement of conditions by which the stock remains at a steady level, as described above. The constants may be determined from a plot of $\log_e R/P$ on P, where $\log_e R/P = 0$, $P = P_r$; the slope of the regression is $-1/P_m$. When $P_r > P_m$, compensatory mechanisms predominate; when $P_r < P_m$, they are less important than the noncompensatory ones. Figure 67 (Ricker, 1958) shows curves of this type for various conditions of recruitment per stock and for various rates of exploitation: the bisector is an essential part of the system because it indicates the point at which stock and recruitment are equal. At a low stock level there is high recruitment and at a high stock level there is low recruitment, which condition expresses once more the principle of compensation. Ricker has attempted to show that this is a real effect by fitting this type of curve to data (from Equation [58]), as he has done for the Tillamook Bay chum salmon (Fig. 68). The fit is fair, but not remarkable; it is clear that a large number of observations would be required before the terms could be determined with any useful degree of accuracy.

Beverton and Holt (1957) have considered that larval mortality has two components, one density dependent and the other density independent:

$$\frac{dN}{dt} = -(\mu_1 + \mu_2 N)N , \qquad (59)$$

where μ_1 is the coefficient of density-independent mortality during a given period of larval life,

     μ_2 is the coefficient of density-dependent mortality during a given period of larval life, and

     N is the number of larvae.

The equation is integrated and developed to the following form:

$$R = \frac{1}{\alpha + \dfrac{\beta}{P_e}}$$

where R is recruitment,

     P_e is egg production or stock, and

     α and β are constants.

One constant describes the total mortality (β) and the other expresses the ratio of density-dependent fraction to the total.

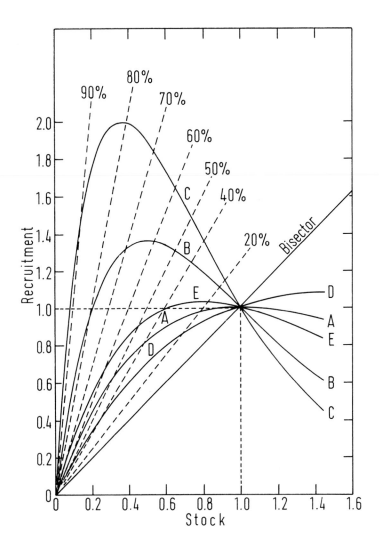

Figure 67. The stock and recruitment curves of Ricker for various conditions. The curves *A–E* represent different "stock and recruitment relationships." They pass through the bisector (where recruitment and stock are equal, and hence recruitment can replace stock) at the same point, an equilibrium point. The dashed lines represent different rates of exploitation. Adapted from Ricker, 1958.

Stock is considered as egg production, because we are concerned with
the relation of stock to subsequent recruitment. But in fitting any
theoretical curve to the data, changes in stock from year to year appear
as variance about the line. Theoretical curves have been fitted to data of
stock and recruitment for the North Sea haddock and the Fraser River
sockeye salmon. They were fitted by plotting the reciprocal of recruitment on that of the parent stock. From the regression of $1/R$ on $1/P$,

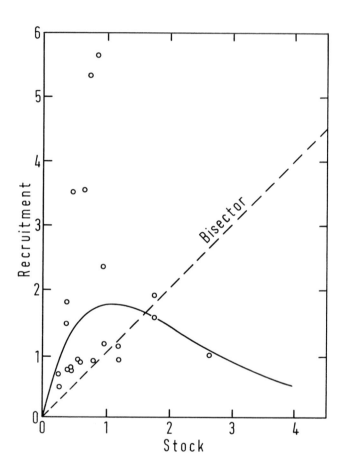

Figure 68. The relationship between recruitment and stock
for the Tillamook Bay chum salmon. The curve is fitted to the
data by using Equation (58), expressing a curve analogous to
those in Figure 67; the rate of exploitation of the Tillamook
Bay salmon was 50 per cent. Adapted from Ricker, 1958.

the constants of the equation (α and β) can be calculated and the curve fitted. The curves reach an asymptote and are not dome-shaped, like those of Ricker. The asymptote implies a wide range of stock within which recruitment is in equilibrium, whereas the dome-shaped curve implies a "maximum carrying capacity" in the environment. For many stocks, the condition at high stock levels is unknown. Further, it is the low levels of stock in which fisheries biologists should really be interested because of the possibilities of recruitment failure. At low levels, both curves are in a sense descriptive, because the true levels of density-dependent mortality and the periods for which they endure are unknown.

Following the work of Graham (1935), Schaefer (1954) has developed a method for estimating maximum sustainable yield (in numbers or in weight), which can be applied to problems of stock and recruitment. The average annual stock in a given year is the mean of the initial stock in January of that year and that in the following January. Consider the average annual stock in numbers in three successive years as P_{n_0}, P_{n_1}, and P_{n_2}. Then the change of initial stock during the year n_1 is given by $(P_{n_2} - P_{n_0})/2$. The quantity $Y_{n_1} + (P_{n_2} - P_{n_0})/2$, where Y_{n_1} is the catch in year n_1, is called the surplus production, P_s. It is an estimate of equilibrium stock. Surplus production may be plotted on stock density, and the data may be fitted with a parabola. Schaefer (1954) gives methods for fitting data of halibut (*Hippoglossus hippoglossus* [Linnaeus]) catches in the northeastern Pacific, using this theory as a basis.

The change of stock $(P_{n_2} - P_{n_0})/2$ is due to annual changes in recruitment and natural mortality (and weight, if stock in weight, P_w, is used). The disadvantage of the method is that the three parameters of growth rate, death rate, and recruitment rate are not separated. Indeed, the method was developed by Schaefer for fishes which cannot be aged, like the tunas, and for which estimates of the above parameters are not readily available. The decline of the blue whale stock (*Sibbaldus musculus* [Linnaeus]) offers the most dramatic application of Schaefer's method (International Commission on Whaling, 1964). In the relationship between stock and recruitment in the blue whale, changes in recruitment are likely to be of greater magnitude than those in natural mortality. Figure 69 shows the relationship between P_s in thousands on stock in thousands between the 1930's and the 1960's. The catches in numbers are shown at the left of the figure. They are all much too high, the stock has fallen below 50,000, and recruitment has declined as a consequence. It is possible that the stock of blue whales has been reduced from about 150,000 before World War II to between

650 and 1,950. There must now be a real risk of extinction. If capture of these whales were to stop now, the stock would take more than 50 years to return to a level at which optimum catches can be made again. It is a great pity that a proper scientific assessment of the remaining stock was not started until 1961.

Rounsefell (1958) has studied the factors causing the decline in sockeye salmon of the Karluk River, Alaska. Figure 70 shows the ratio of recruitment to stock (in logarithms) plotted on the stock in numbers. This is the same type of method as shown in Figure 63. The logarithmic relationship is linear, allowing statistical treatment to be exploited. Rounsefell has done this by correlating the deviations from the line with environmental factors. When a significant correlation was found,

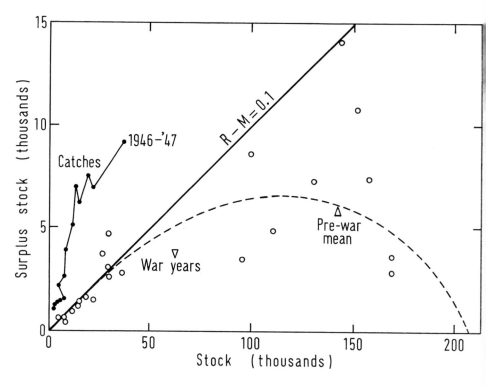

Figure 69. The relationship between surplus stock and stock for the Antarctic blue whale, according to M. B. Schaefer's method for estimating maximum sustainable yield. The dashed line gives the curve fitted to the data by eye from stock numbers over 50,000. The solid line of plotted points represents the declining catches in numbers from 1946–47 to 1960. In $R - M = 0.1$, R is the rate of recruitment (as proportion of stock), and M is the natural mortality rate (here the number of deaths per year as a proportion of stock). Adapted from International Commission on Whaling, 1964.

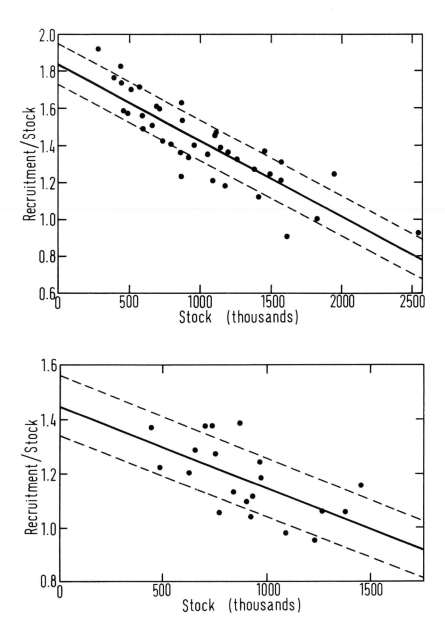

Figure 70. Recruitment/stock in logarithms plotted on stock in numbers of the Karluk River sockeye salmon, corrected for a number of environmental factors. *Top:* 1887–1923. *Bottom:* 1924–48. The solid line represents a linear regression fitted to the data. The dashed lines represent 95 per cent confidence limits to the line. Adapted from Rounsefell, 1958.

the deviations were corrected and a new relationship was set up between return per spawner and stock. The following factors were successfully treated in succession:

(1) water temperature in autumn on egg survival;

(2) length of growing season on larval survival;

(3) spring temperatures on emergence of fry;

(4) rainfall on the survival of fry;

(5) the effect of odd and even years (because the sockeye only spawns successfully in even years in the Karluk River);

(6) the numbers of two-year-old and three-year-old fish on the numbers of the fry (this is presumably the result of density-dependent predation).

This work has been quoted rather fully because it uses a technique that reveals some of the structure of larval survival. It is unlikely that the nature of the compensatory mechanism will be unraveled with the use of this method, but some of the confusing variances will be removed.

Summary

The problem of the relationship between parent stock and subsequent recruitment is the hardest one in fisheries biology to solve. Two sorts of data are lacking: (1), long-time series of estimates of stock and recruitment; and (2), a range of measures of larval and juvenile mortality at sea. Both sets of data could be used to understand the nature of the compensatory mechanism. It is likely that the essence of the mechanism is a form of density-dependent mortality, which may operate like Hjort's critical period.

The proper description of the mechanism will not only answer the fishermen's question about the effect of fishing on brood survival, but will go straight to the root of the dramatic fluctuations in stock in the great fisheries.

9 | The Oceanic Boundaries

THE ocean appears to be featureless. With their range of vision limited by the physical properties of seawater to a sphere with a radius of 30–200 ft, fish see only a few food targets at any one time. There are well-defined physical structures in the waters of the ocean, and fish populations sometimes gather there. There are three associated facts— the short range of perception, the long range of migration among some species, and the presence of shoals at the oceanic boundaries. It is possible that migrant fish use the oceanic boundaries as a means of achieving their migrations. There are three main oceanic boundaries:

(1) isotherms that limit the range of the fish and that are sharp enough to generate changes in behavior;

(2) current boundaries against which the fish pack, perhaps for food, perhaps mechanically, or perhaps because they see them;

(3) an area of upwelling or divergence, where water from below rises to the surface, where plankton production is often intense, and where fish gather.

Fish concentrate at each of these boundaries. The causes of concentration are examined below, where they affect the concepts of fisheries biology. The most important of these is the idea of a unit stock, insofar as oceanic boundaries might really be stock boundaries. In the upwelling areas are found the best conditions for the survival of larvae and juveniles which would illuminate the problem of stock and recruitment. Four problems that relate to fisheries biology are discussed: the restriction of the arctic cod by the 2°C isotherm on the seabed; the relation of tuna to current boundaries; the relation of herring to horizontal boundaries; and the production of fish in the upwelling areas.

Fish are caught where they are concentrated. They gather at some point on their migration circuit to spawn, to feed, or to take advantage of the current structure in achieving their migrations. The arctic cod and the Pacific tuna gather at oceanic boundaries perhaps to feed at the best advantage. Such advantage is certainly present when the North Sea herring pack against the Baltic outflow in early spring. Fisheries are established at such boundaries because the fish live there during part of their migration cycles. In the great upwelling regions, the whole life of sardine-like fishes may be geared to the food production system. The structure of the ocean is moderately well known. From the nature of migration circuits and the dependence of fish on productive cycles, fisheries biologists need to know the courses of the oceanic currents.

The Arctic Cod and the 2°C Isotherm on the Bottom

It was shown in Chapter 3 (Richardson et al., 1959) that, in midsummer on the Svalbard shelf, the arctic cod do not appear to cross the 2°C isotherm on the bottom or the same isotherm in midwater during spring and autumn in the southeastern Barents Sea (Hylen et al., 1961). Figures 71 and 72 contrast a survey of trawl catches and bottom temperatures made in early June 1949 with a similar one made in late May and early June 1950 (Lee, 1952). In 1950 cold water lay close to Bear Island, and in 1949 it was spread to the very edge of the Svalbard shelf. In both cruises, the best catches were found in water warmer than 2°C, regardless of depth. The same results were obtained on a number of occasions (Lee, 1952). It is worth pointing out that the catches were heavy, that British trawlers steamed 1,500 miles to crowd on the Svalbard shelf in summer to form what the fishermen called "arctic cities."

Figure 24 shows three echo surveys (Richardson et al., 1959) that were made within a fortnight of each other; they described the movement of cod onto the shelf, and in each survey the echo traces of cod were bounded by the 2°C isotherm on the bottom. On the western edge of the Svalbard shelf, there are two submarine inlets, the Størfjordrenna, south of Spitsbergen, and the Northwest Gully, north of Bear Island. The Størfjordrenna was flooded with cold water that had drifted on the bottom down the east side of Spitsbergen. The Northwest Gully was flooded with warm water that had pushed up from the West Spitsbergen current. On the first echo survey, the cold concentrations were bounded neatly by the 2°C isotherm. Within a fortnight, on the third survey, the cod patches had moved up the shelf from about 150 fm to about 80 fm. At the same time, the 2°C isotherm had moved up the shelf to the same extent. Some six weeks later a further survey (Beverton and Lee, 1964) was made over the whole of the Svalbard shelf, and the 2° C isotherm had spread to its eastern edge. The echo patches of cod had diffused over the area, and there were no longer any dense concentrations worth fishing.

Since dispersion would ordinarily be expected after a movement of three or four hundred miles, the concentration actually found might at first seem surprising. The question is whether the cod were thrown mechanically onto the shelf by the upward movement of the warmer water or whether they were concentrated against the cold-water barrier by some physiological factor. The estimated quantity shown in Figure 24 might be a fair fraction of the spawning stock, which had migrated back from the Vest Fjord. But, the cold-water mass from the Størfjordrenna extends into the ocean, and might prevent northward movements by the fish, thus making a "traffic jam." Whatever is the cause of the movement, two facts emerge: (1) the fish concentrate against the 2° C isotherm on the seabed; and (2) as the temperature boundary recedes eastward, the fish diffuse over the shelf.

In the early summer season, the cod appear to suffer if they find themselves in water colder than 2° C. Woodhead and Woodhead (1959) have found that cod taken from water colder than 2° C have more chloride in their blood than those taken from water warmer than 2° C. In the colder water, then, the chloride-secreting cells in the gills were not functioning properly, in spite of the fact that these cells proliferate in fish in cold water. Salt excretion is a necessary function in marine teleosts, and it should not fail.

It is possible that later in the summer, when the cod feed heavily, they move more readily into the cold water. But the real point is that in June, after a long migration with little food, when the fish do not cross the cold-water boundary, they might be uncomfortable if they did.

The concentration of fish may thus be based on a form of kinesis, if the temperature barrier were sharp enough. As fish swim more slowly in cooler water, so they gather in patches. But this hypothesis does not explain why cod are not found at all in the really colder water. In the sea, temperature barriers are often not very sharp, the fish having to swim considerable distances before encountering a noticeable temperature change. But on the western Svalbard shelf in June, the temperature barrier can be fairly sharp—as much as 1.5° C in a mile (Lee, 1952). Fish are sensitive to a change in temperature of 0.03° C (Bull, 1936), and since 70-cm cod can cruise at 4.2 knots (Harden Jones, 1963) they could detect changes every 20 sec on a straight

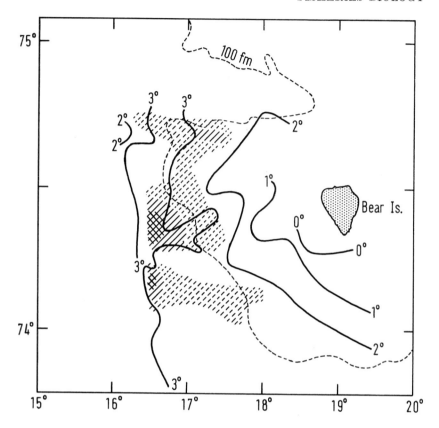

Figure 71. Cod catches and bottom temperatures west of Bear Island from 27
May to 5 June 1950. Distribution of cod catches are presented with respect to
the 2° C isotherm on the bottom. Seabed temperatures were recorded at the end
of each haul, and contours are of isotherms on the bottom. The differently
hatched areas indicate where the highest catches of cod were obtained. Adapted
from Lee, 1952.

course. There is perhaps enough sensory information received by the
fish to allow them to gather as the water gets colder. Such a minimal
mechanism would allow the fish to gather in patches close to the cold-
water boundary.

Tuna and the Current Boundaries

The Gulf Stream and the Kuroshio are fast currents with sharp
boundaries. The current is fast at the boundary because the latter is
the edge of an oceanic gyre, and Stommel (1958) has shown that, in the

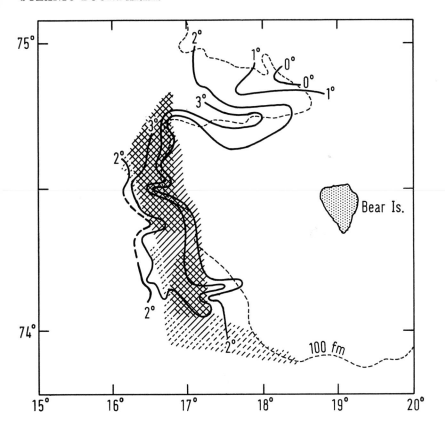

Figure 72. Cod catches and bottom temperatures west of Bear Island from 31 May to 6 June 1949. Distribution of cod catches are presented with respect to the 2° C isotherm on the bottom. Seabed temperatures were recorded at the end of each haul, and contours are of isotherms on the bottom. The differently hatched areas indicate where the highest catches of cod were obtained. Adapted from Lee, 1952.

northern hemisphere, currents are swifter on the western side of an ocean. Uda (1959) has found that the boundaries within the oceans are good places to fish because of the concentrations, particularly of sardine-like fish, that occur there; the Japanese fishermen call these edges "siome," which can be seen at the surface or even heard as one opposing surface rubs against another.

At the Equator, there are two main currents—the North Equatorial current westbound between 10° N and 18° N, and the South Equatorial current westbound between 2° S and 14° S. Between them in the

Pacific runs an Equatorial countercurrent eastbound between 5° N and 10° N. Between the countercurrent and the South Equatorial current, there are zones of divergence and convergence. A zone of divergence is one where water rises from below and diverges in the surface layer; conversely, a zone of convergence is one where water sinks from surfaces that converge toward each other. Divergence and convergence are to some extent complementary aspects of the same phenomenon.

King and Hida (1957) found that the yellowfin tuna (*Thunnus albacares* [Bonnaterre]) occurred in the zones of both convergence and divergence of the Pacific equatorial currents, and that the catches were between two and three times greater than in the main currents (Fig. 73). The zooplankton volumes are greater in these zones, but only marginally so, as compared with the South Equatorial current in the second half of the year, or with the Equatorial countercurrent in the first half. It might be thought that the yellowfin aggregate on the zooplankton, but they feed on rather larger animals—fishes the size of sardines or myctophids (Legendre, 1934)—which, in turn, feed on zooplankton. The tuna must aggregate transversely across the currents into the zones of divergence and convergence. The process of aggregation implies the existence of a reservoir from which the fish can move to concentrate, and the equatorial currents may well provide this. It is often thought that divergence generates more nutrients, which produce more zooplankton. If this was actually the case, the zone of convergence should be sterile, which it is not.

Murphy and Shomura (1955) have shown that the degree of aggregation of the yellowfin tuna depends on the temperature structure of the water. When the zone of divergence is narrow, the fish are tightly packed, but when the cool water is spread over a wide area, there is little aggregation.

The boundaries along the Equator are complex, and the mechanisms of fish aggregation there are not fully understood; neither is readily explained in terms of simple associations. There are two ways in which the mechanisms could be elucidated—a study of the causes of aggregation, and an examination of the means by which the tuna migrate.

The Herring and Its Boundaries

One of the first pieces of research carried out by the Norwegians after World War II resulted in the discovery of herring offshore in the Norwegian Sea in winter, before they reached the traditional grounds close to the coast (Devold, 1952). In later years the work was extended to the whole Norwegian Sea and at other seasons than midwinter. From

21 May to 30 June 1954, sonar and temperature surveys were made
(Fig. 74) by research vessels from Denmark, Iceland, and Norway
(Tåning, Einarsson, and Eggvin, 1955). The temperature distribution
conveniently describes a complex oceanic state. The warm Atlantic
current moves between the Shetland Islands and the Faeroes along
the Norwegian coast; in the northern Norwegian Sea, it breaks into the
West Spitsbergen current and the North Cape current. The synoptic
temperature distribution also describes a cold mass of water between
Iceland, Greenland, and Jan Mayen. Off the east coast of Iceland, the

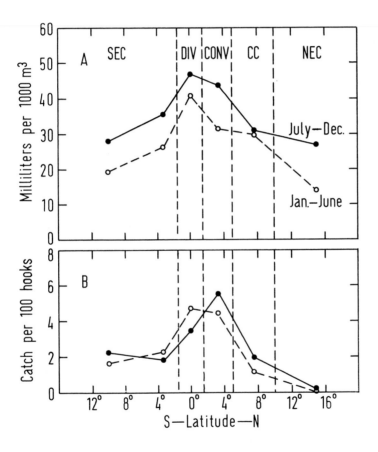

Figure 73. Catches of zooplankton (*A*) and of yellowfin tuna (*B*)
in a transect across the Equator. SEC = South Equatorial current;
DIV = zone of divergence; CONV = zone of convergence; CC
= countercurrent; NEC = North Equatorial current. Adapted from
King and Hida, 1957.

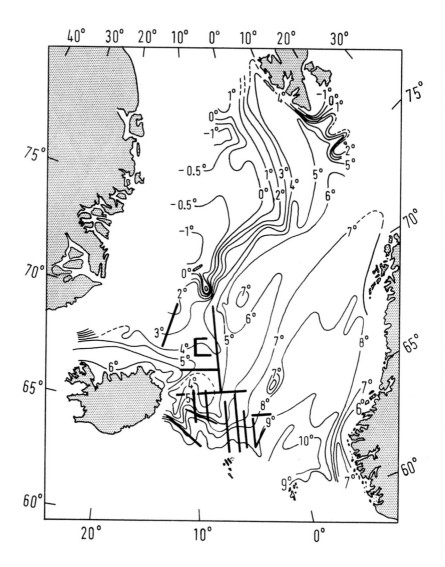

Figure 74. The concentration of herring at a boundary in the Norwegian Sea between 21 May and 30 June 1954. The bold black lines represent the presence of fish, as shown by sonar and echo-sounder records. The temperature observations were made at 20 m. Adapted from Tåning, Einarsson, and Eggvin, 1955.

warm Atlantic water in the Irminger current makes a sharp boundary with the cooler water, near which the herring sonar traces were found. To the north, extensive traces were found over a wide area of cool water. There is no simple relation between herring and temperature, because the fish are found in dense patches at all temperatures from 2° C to 9° C, which is the total range of temperature in the Norwegian Sea during the period of survey. Yet the distribution of sonar traces bears some relation to the current structure as outlined by the temperature distribution. Later in the year, the sonar traces move eastward toward the Norwegian coast and then appear to "punch" their way through the warm-water barrier of the Atlantic extension. The problem is complex and a simple interpretation does not seem applicable, because the nature of the migratory mechanism is not understood.

Another boundary at which herring gather has been described by Steele (1961) in the eastern North Sea in spring. The deep water off the Norwegian coast is overlaid by the Baltic outflow, flowing north. The outflow of cold, somewhat fresh water at the surface forms a stable layer on top of the saltier, but warmer, North Sea water. Because the layer is stable there is little vertical turbulence, in sharp contrast to the North Sea itself in March and April. Consequently the productive cycle starts much earlier in the Baltic outflow than it does in the open North Sea. Echo traces (probably of herring) were packed on the edge of the Baltic outflow, where both chlorophyll content and quantity of zooplankton were high. The fish appeared to live in the daytime below the Baltic outflow and migrate upward at night to feed on euphausiids and *Calanus*; the herring tended to stay on the western edge of the outflow, possibly because the euphausiids remained on the edge of the deep water off Norway, which coincided with the edge of the Baltic outflow. An apparently simple association of echo trace (or herring) and surface temperature is probably the consequence of a rather complex mechanism.

Upwelling

With the term "upwelling" used in a broad sense to include divergences and other oceanic processes, some of the areas of upwelling important to fisheries are shown in Figure 75. This is Townsend's (1935) chart of the positions of sperm whale (*Physeter catodon* Linnaeus) catches which were logged by whalers working from Nantucket, Massachusetts, between 1729 and 1919. From October to March there were four main areas of catching which have been identified as upwelling areas—in the Humboldt current along the western coast of South America, in the Benguela current along the western coast of South

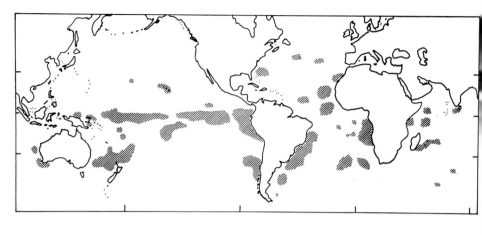

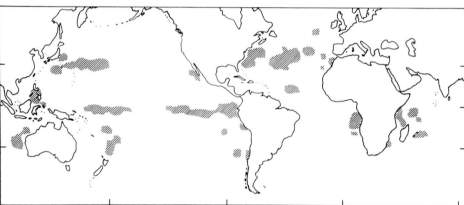

Figure 75. Positions of sperm whales taken by Nantucket, Massachusetts, whalers from 1729 to 1919. *Top:* October–March. *Bottom:* April–September. From Townsend, 1935.

Africa, off Cape Verde, and along the Equator; there was another area off the southern coast of Somalia. From April to September, in addition to the Equator and the Benguela areas, there was another near the Kuroshio extension east of Japan. Many are areas of upwelling, but there are others which are not, like the Sargasso and the area just off Nantucket.* Townsend's picture is one of the simplest ways of representing the upwelling areas, presumably because the sperm whales aggregate on the fish stocks gathered there.

---

* These two areas may have been searched much more systematically than others, because the whalers had to cross both areas when leaving and returning to Nantucket.

One of the most productive fisheries in the world is that for the anchoveta (*Engraulis ringens* Jenyns) in the Humboldt current off Peru and northern Chile (Jordan and de Vildoso, 1965). In 1965, 7 million tons were landed. The cold Humboldt current from the sub-antarctic region sweeps north along the South American coast, and wells up against the continental shelf between Peru and the Galapagos Islands. Where the cold water reaches the surface, the plankton becomes dense and the fish gather. Every few years off the northern coast of Peru a warm current appears, called "El Niño" because it comes at Christmas, the season of the Christ child. As it moves south, it destroys the cold-water plankton. The plankton rots in the water, and off Callão a sulfurous emanation is produced, known as the "Callão Painter," which stains the white paint of ships, tarnishes silver in coastal homes, and may even kill large numbers of fish and birds. A major fisheries problem in Peru is to determine whether there are enough anchoveta for both the fishing industry and the guano industry. The guano industry depends on the populations of the three species of birds living on the Peruvian islands—cormorants, boobies, and pelicans. In 1958, when El Niño came in, the bird populations were sharply reduced. By 1962, however, they had fully recovered. The anchoveta stock, feeding partly on phytoplankton, must supply enough fish annually for 30 million birds as well as the catch of 7 million tons taken by the fishermen. The recovery in the stock of the guano-producing birds took place at a time when the fishery was increasing sharply. Hence, up to 1962, it is unlikely that the guano industry has suffered too severely from competition with the fishery.

The same type of problem connecting guano production with a fishery is found in the Benguela current where there are three sardine fisheries—at St. Helena Bay in South Africa, Walvis Bay in South-West Africa, and Baia dos Tigres in Angola (Davies, 1957). Between 200 thousand and 300 thousand tons of South African pilchard (*Sardinops ocellata* Pappé) and 80 thousand tons of maasbanker (*Trachurus trachurus* [Linnaeus]) are caught each year (Davies, 1957). Figure 76 shows the mechanism of upwelling in the Benguela current (Hart and Currie, 1960). The main current drives north, and a compensating current runs south. Above this main current, the upwelling water extends far offshore under the influence of southerly winds. Where the cold water reaches the surface, plankton becomes very dense; in Walvis Bay, for example, it can become so dense as to rot on the shoreline in heaps. To produce 1.6 thousand tons of guano annually in this area (Fig. 77), the guano-producing penguins, gannets, and cormorants consume 43 thousand tons of pilchard and 7 thousand tons of maasbanker (Davies,

1958). The fisheries annually account for an additional 200–400
thousand tons of pilchard and maasbanker. The proportion of the
number of fish taken by birds is not only interesting in itself, but con-
stitutes one of the first steps in a study of the cause of natural mortality.

The central problem in a study of upwelling is how the huge fish
stocks are generated, how their numbers are maintained, and how the
fish remain in the same position. In the deep tropical ocean far from the
upwelling zones, the water is very clear and the plankton is very thin.
The appearance of cold water at the surface generates dense plankton
outbursts, either because the water is cold, or because it is rich in nu-

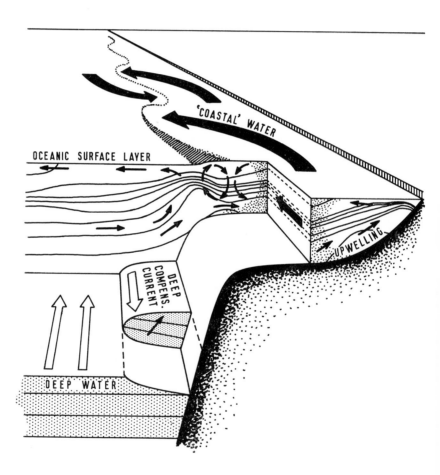

Figure 76. The mechanism of upwelling in the Benguela current off the southwestern coast of Africa. Adapted from Hart and Currie, 1960.

trients, or both. A stable cycle ($\times$ 10 in amplitude) of plankton production in deep tropical oceans far from the upwelling areas may be
contrasted with what has been described as an unstable, or unbalanced,
cycle ($\times$ 100 or more in amplitude) in temperate waters (Cushing,
1959*b*). The difference between the two cycles is that the temperate one
does not operate in winter, whereas the tropical cycle is continuous; so,
when the temperate one starts again in spring, the plant and animal
components are out of phase with each other. The plants grow to very
high densities before the animal populations, which control them by
grazing, have a chance to increase in numbers. The productive cycle
in an upwelling area resembles the temperate cycle in that the whole
cycle starts from very low initial numbers; the appearance of cold
water at the surface is analogous to the temperate spring. Hence, the
cold water and the initially sparse plankton are sufficient to account
for the subsequent dense outburst. At this stage, the accompanying
rich nutrients are perhaps irrelevant; but at a later stage they may be

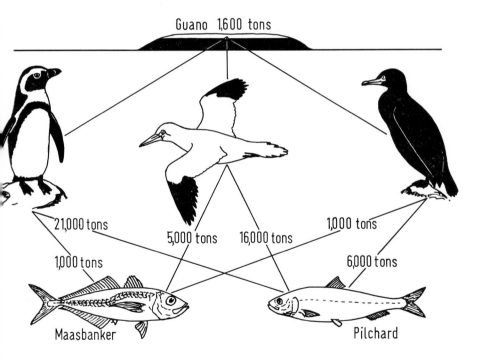

Guano 1,600 tons

21,000 tons

5,000 tons   16,000 tons

1,000 tons

1,000 tons

6,000 tons

Maasbanker   Pilchard

Figure 77. Some natural enemies of the pilchard and maasbanker in the Benguela current
ff the southwestern coast of Africa. The guano-producing birds are a species of penguin, the
annet, and one of the cormorants. Adapted from Davies, 1958.

important. There is some evidence in temperate waters that the spring outburst is controlled less by lack of nutrients than by grazing (Cushing and Nicholson, 1963). By keeping zooplankton-free water in a large plastic bag hung at the ocean surface, McAllister et al. (1960) have shown that the algal quantities increased by many times. Hence, the low algal quantities in the deep ocean must be controlled at that low level by the grazing animals. In temperate waters, however, nutrients decline after the spring outburst, being absorbed principally as animal flesh and possibly limiting subsequent production. In upwelling areas, there is a continuous presence of nutrients after the first outburst. High production thus appears to be maintained continuously at the point of upwelling, the subsequent cycles supposedly decaying at a distance as the upwelled water drifts out into the deep ocean.

Fish can either aggregate from elsewhere to the upwelling region or the year classes can build up at the point of upwelling as a result of the larvae drifting with the plankton. Nothing is known decisively of the migratory habits of fish in the upwelling areas, but it seems unlikely that they aggregate from elsewhere, because upwelling is a more or less continuous process, at least in the Humboldt and Benguela currents. Hence, food for larval fish is permanently available. Large recruit classes have been built up at very high stock levels. Knowledge of the migratory cycle is still needed, but one would guess that the baby fish grow up, not close inshore like North Sea juvenile herring, but offshore where the plankton is very dense. Hence, when food is superabundant, the recruit classes are strong.

Summary

The nature of some aggregations at oceanic boundaries has been examined under a number of conditions. The concentration of cod against the 2° C isotherm on the seabed is described in some detail, and a physiological basis for the aggregation is suggested. A proper and full description of the mechanisms involved must await further study. Such mechanisms are at the base of the cod's migratory pattern and the 2° C isotherm forms a reliable edge to the stock area of the arctic cod in the Barents Sea.

For tuna and herring, there are simple associations of fish and temperature, which probably are indicators of more complex mechanisms. It is likely that the aggregation of yellowfin tuna at the Equator is one of these complex mechanisms. That causing the aggregation of herring on the edge of the Baltic outflow in early spring is discussed to some extent. The fisheries biologist is interested not only in the mechanisms themselves, but in the underlying reasons for the dependence of a stock like the North Sea herring on the edge of the Baltic outflow each year as a part of its regular mode of life. The mechanisms and their relationships to the stocks, when understood, will provide the biological bases of stock unities.

The examination of upwelling areas provides many opportunities for speculation. In such areas, the structure of productive cycles should be closely examined, together with the migratory pattern of the dominant fishes. Some progress has already been made in analyzing causes of natural mortality for the South African pilchard. Further, the anchoveta fishery off Peru may provide good opportunities for studying the problem of stock and recruitment because of the periodical extensive stock changes associated with El Niño.

Due to the vastness of the oceans, extensive surveys have been more or less crude, and have thus far yielded little more than the rough associations described above. In each of the associations, the fisheries biologist will find complex mechanisms, as in the study of the arctic cod, the North Sea herring, or the yellowfin tuna. The enquiry needed is one based on the disciplines of fisheries biology.

10 | The Future of Fisheries Research

IF the outcome of any research project could be safely predicted, there would be no need for research. Earlier chapters have been concerned with what is fairly well established in the recorded present knowledge of fisheries biology. Some recapitulation of subjects discussed earlier in this volume is necessary, since these same subjects form the foundation and framework on which to base research for the future.

Migration

The study of migration is fundamental to the biology of fisheries research because it explains why stocks remain in the same region and why they retain their unity from generation to generation. The study of migration today consists of two major parts: the study of navigation (as a method of determining position and course) and the study of fish movements. Work on navigation by fish has been confined to a study of orientation in two sensory channels. Hasler (1954) has examined the olfactory sense of the Pacific salmon, as relevant to migrational studies. He has also shown (Hasler and Schwassmann, 1960) that fish have the capacity to orientate by the sun. In a circular tank, fish were trained to select a segment at a specified angle to the sun, so that on entering the tank the fish went to this particular segment, irrespective of time of day. Selection of this segment persisted even after the fish had been transported from Madison, Wisconsin, where the experiment originated, to about the same latitude south of the Equator. Knowledge of a capacity to orient to an external referent is needed before "navigation" can be used; the object may be a river, the smell of which can be detected at sea, an island, detected by the roar of breakers, or it may even be the sun.

The sensory channels of fish have been studied for many years. Threshold sensitivities to temperature and salinity were measured by Bull (1936), using the conditioned-reflex technique. Threshold values for angular and linear accelerations have been established by Harden Jones (1957b), and Clarke (1936) has estimated thresholds for light sensitivity. Experiments have been conducted on the responses of fish to moving backgrounds (Harden Jones, 1963), to water currents, and to light and temperature gradients (Woodhead, 1965). A number of adequate reviews on the subject are available, e.g., Harden Jones (1960).

Such work explores the capacity of fish to use particular sensory channels, but does little to explore their capacity to ignore such information. Tagging can be used to study fish movements, and the results show the shortest distance between the point of liberation and the point of recapture, and hence a minimum estimate of speed and a biased estimate of direction. However, in the case of the North Sea herring, it was useful to find that the migratory direction of adult fish corresponded with that of drift of the main North Sea swirl. Such a valuable discovery resulted from the data of a rather simple tagging experiment where the recaptures were tabulated by time and place of recovery (Höglund, 1955; see Table 3 in Chapter 2). But the drift in the water is more apparent than real, because the herring reach their spawning grounds each year at rather precise times; it is as if the fish take their direction from the drift of water, but not their timing. To understand how fish achieve this end, their movements must be known in detail—how they migrate at different depths by day and by night, how quickly they move from position to position, and how the currents move at the same time. Some work has been done with salmon equipped with an ultrasonic tag that allows detailed individual movements to be tracked for short distances (Johnson, 1960).

Tagging will rarely answer all of these questions. Harden Jones (1957a) has tried to analyze the positions of herring shoals in a tidal stream between the Sandettié and Ruytingen banks in the southern North Sea; the area is a well-known spawning ground. Movements of the fish shoals were recorded by means of a continuously running echo sounder over a predetermined series of tracks made by the ship up and down tide, and by a Decca track plotter that traced the ship's transects. Figure 78 illustrates the change of position of the shoals in relation to time and space (Harden Jones, 1957a). From this work,

Harden Jones concluded that some shoals of herring appeared to drift completely with the tide, whereas some others (probably of spawning fish) appeared to hold their own against rather swift tidal streams.

Recently, a sector-scanning sonar has been used to make a preliminary analysis of the detailed movement of fish shoals (Harden Jones

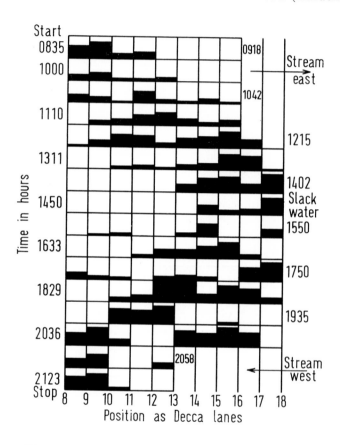

Figure 78. The movement of fish shoals, probably of herring, in a tidal stream. Distance is shown on the abscissa as "lanes" recorded by the Decca navigator; these are numbered on the chart, 8–18. Time is represented on the left and right of the diagram, reading downward from 0835 hr. The ship's track ran up and down tide, across the Decca navigational lanes. Times shown on the left and right of the diagram are the times of turning. The tidal cycle is also recorded in time, slack water occurring at 1430 hr. The fish shoals are shown as histograms of echo density in time and space, and the shoals are shown to be moving with the tidal stream. Adapted from Harden Jones, 1957a.

and McCartney, 1962). A large transducer, with seven independent sections, was operated at 37 kHz. With one section, sound was transmitted over a wide beam, and was received on all sections; the narrow receiver beam was steered electronically. Imagine a target at a considerable angle to the axis of the transmitted beam. Signals are received from this target by each of the sections. The range of the target at each section is slightly different, and therefore the phase of the received plane wave is different at each section. The received amplitudes of each section differing in phase are resolved into measurable differences in frequency. It is then possible to resolve the information according to bearing and range. If the targets are fish targets, probably small shoals in one transmission, they appear at different positions on successive transmissions. Hence, from an anchored ship they can be observed crossing the beam. The results of such a series of observations can be presented as a polar diagram (Fig. 79). The general trend of movement is in the direction of the tide, the current of which is measured by a current meter suspended from the anchored ship; it is interesting to notice that a few targets appear to move against the tide and that many move at an apparent angle to the tide.

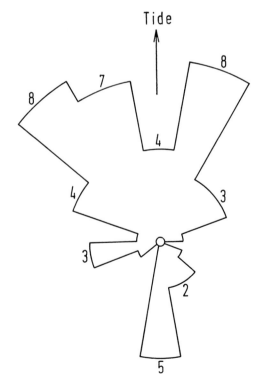

Tide

Figure 79. A polar diagram of the results of sector-scanning observations. The numbers represent the number of targets, or fish shoals, recorded traveling in the directions indicated in relation to the tidal current. Adapted from Harden Jones and McCartney, 1962.

New techniques, such as the one just described, and further experimental work with sensory channels are going to provide the type of information now needed for a more complete understanding of fish migration.

Stock Density

Another fundamental approach to fisheries biology concerns the study of abundance. As observed in earlier chapters, the catch per unit of effort is a proper index of stock, but it can become biased by effects of availability. Independent measures of stock are therefore needed, such as estimates based on egg counts. The egg-counting technique only works in checking the stock densities on or near spawning grounds. When only part of the stock is present, as for example on a feeding ground, no independent measure of stock density can be made. In such a situation, it is possible to use echo-sounding. Richardson et al. (1959) were able to relate stock density of cod with echo voltage measured at a distance of 1 fm above the bottom (Fig. 80). The voltages

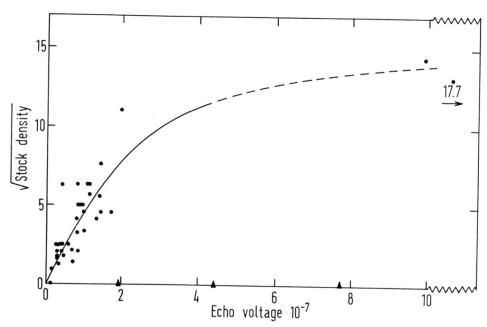

Figure 80. Relationship between stock density of cod (transformed by the square root) and echo voltage (as at a distance of 1 fm from the transducer, so differences in depth are corrected). At the three points on the abscissa, shown as solid triangles, when no catch was made even though high levels of signal amplitude were recorded, the fish were probably swimming just above the trawl. Adapted from Richardson et al., 1959.

are raised by the square of the depth to eliminate depth differences; the stock densities are expressed as square roots because, within a wavelength or a sound pulse, the amplitude (or voltage) from a small group of targets, like a little shoal of cod, is proportional to the square root of the numbers. The relationship is variable, but, in general, the higher the signal, the higher the catch. There are some ambiguities in depth resolution with a wide-beam echo sounder, and fish which appear close to the bottom on the echo record can, in fact, be above the head-line of the trawl. The predominance of cod on the Svalbard shelf, where these operations were conducted, made much of the work rather simple.

There is some promise of being able to count fish with an echo sounder, and it would also be desirable to estimate their sizes acoustically. Figure 81 (adapted from Cushing, 1964b, based on data of Midttun and Hoff, 1962, and Cushing et al., 1963) shows the target strength of fish as a function of length (in logarithms). Target strength is a term expressing signal in decibels with reference to a unit of pressure, 1 μbar. Single fish of different sizes could be resolved by an echo sounder merely in terms of their target strength. However, it is an accident that fish sizes often approximate the wavelength of sound used in commercial echo sounders. Below one-quarter wavelength, sound is scattered according to Rayleigh's law (i.e., target strength varies inversely as the fourth power of the frequency); above two or three wavelengths, sound is reflected geometrically. In the middle zone between the scattering and geometric zones, sound is reflected or scattered in a complex way. By means of carefully scaled-down model experiments, Haslett (1962) has been able to define the lower limit of the middle zone in length as about eight fish lengths per wavelength.

The techniques described above may be combined. With a sector scanner working at high enough frequency to resolve fish shoals into individuals, it should become possible to count and size fish targets. But such techniques cannot identify fish as species, and there may often be confusion between fish species of about the same size—for example, herring and pilchard.

A second aspect of the study of abundance concerns the adequate sampling of biological material. Each year 750,000 fish are measured on the quays of English ports. This large number tends to discourage further expansion of individual measurements. Most fish species caught are subjected to a sampling system. From the samples, estimates of Z, K, and L_∞ are made, but those for F or M are not obtained as easily. Fisheries biologists have not kept a particularly close watch on changes in efficiency of the fleets, nor have they attempted to investigate the interrelationships of stocks or environmental effects on the basic parameters.

Equipment for the automatic handling of data is available and is now starting to save time. The automatic processing of data, when first obtained, is needed in order to reduce the costs of sampling, counting eggs, counting vertebrae, measuring l_1 distributions, estimating

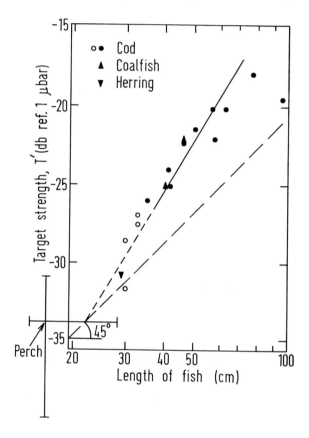

Figure 81. Relationship between target strength (in decibels with reference to a unit of pressure, 1 μbar) and length of fish (in logarithms). Adapted from Cushing, 1964*b*; data from Midttun and Hoff, 1962, and Cushing et al., 1963. The observation on perch, with indicated errors in observation in a small tank, was made by Jones and Pearce, 1958. The full line represents the line fitted to Midttun and Hoff's original data. The long-dashed line represents the proportional line, expected if target strength were a function of cross-sectional area.

fat, etc. It used to take 2 days to take a fat measurement with a Soxhlet apparatus; now it takes 20 min with an infrared weighing balance. It used to take 3 days to count the eggs in one ovary; now it takes 15 min with an automatic counter (Parrish, Baxter, and Mowat, 1960). There are a number of biological measurements, such as those for fat, fecundity, vertebral sum, and maturity, that are not part of the general sampling program. When mechanical handling becomes more established, such characters will be routinely and efficiently estimated.

In a consideration of environmental effects, a choice must be made of which piece of a multifarious environment to examine. Much has been made of the dependence of North Sea herring fisheries on stock densities of *Calanus*. Herring do feed on *Calanus* predominantly, and a long series of observations on *Calanus* abundance in the North Sea is available. A relationship was established between herring growth and *Calanus* density, but there may well be other relationships, unknown because time series of other observations are not available. The same case could be made for the proper measurements of currents in any sea area. To understand fish movements, we need to know more about water movements, in some detail and routinely, over a long period. What is needed is extensive sampling of many parameters and characters, but care must be taken in selecting the characters to be measured.

Perhaps the most imaginative outlook into the future is that arising from the study of stock and recruitment. The first part of this new perspective derives from the work of Shelbourne at Lowestoft. Toward the end of the nineteenth century, the problems of overfishing would have been solved by building fish hatcheries. Unhappily, they rarely worked because the fish were released not long after hatching, and the benefit that would have derived from numbers of recruited adults should have been divided by the fecundity of the adults. Consequently, the cost of artificial recruitment on an effective scale in the sea was prohibitive. Plaice larvae can be readily reared beyond metamorphosis (Shelbourne, 1963; Shelbourne, Riley, and Thacker, 1963). If the larvae are not immediately successful when they first have to start feeding in a natural environment, they face the danger of the chloride-secreting cells in their gills not working properly (Shelbourne, 1956). The animal depends on food of a critical size, not too small and not too big. If the larvae are short of food, they fall victims to osmotic hazards and lose chloride, and in development they become literally twisted. Shelbourne found that the baby plaice could be tided over this critical period by feeding them on the nauplii of *Artemia*, which are of the right size for the larval plaice and are readily available.

His next step was to examine means of producing young plaice in quantity. Two essential stages were necessary. The first was the employment of large sessile algae to maintain the gas balance; the young larvae, densely packed, excrete carbon dioxide into the seawater in large quantities, which are taken up readily by the algae. Figure 82 shows the experimental apparatus developed to achieve this end

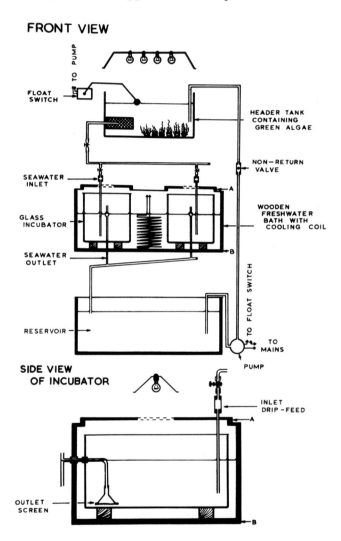

Figure 82. The closed-circulation apparatus used for rearing young plaice to an age of three months. From Shelbourne et al., 1963.

(Shelbourne et al., 1963). The second stage involved the use of anti-
biotics to keep under control the bacteria that develop rapidly on the
surfaces of any tank system. In the spring of 1962, Shelbourne was able
to rear 25,000 plaice to the age of about three months, with a survival
rate of 60 per cent. This is a notable achievement, and it is possible
that a million fish could be raised to the age of three months in about
300 little tanks occupying 350 square feet of space.

There are two consequences of this remarkable development. The
first is that there are two possible commercial implications. Recruitment could be artificially augmented to the benefit of fishermen, or
plaice could be reared in something like a broiler factory. The second
consequence is of more general scope scientifically. The California
Cooperative Fisheries Investigation workers have concluded that perhaps the best way to study the stock and recruitment problem in the
California sardine is to encourage a fishery for the jack mackerel
(*Trachurus symmetricus* [Ayres]), the sardine's main competitor. The
intensive study of fish culture lends itself to an extension of understanding the problem of how fish populations maintain themselves
naturally, the problem of stock and recruitment.

The same remarks can be made about the Russian transplantation
experiments, which were perhaps direct consequences of Nikolsky's
(1953) examination of fecundity differences between different regions.
Indeed, when Baltic herring were transplanted to the Caspian Sea,
very high survival rates were found, which resulted in the establishment
of a fishery from very low numbers of transplants. The Russians have
transplanted pink salmon to the Atlantic, and the fish have appeared
in European rivers. Again, Shelbourne's technique could facilitate
transplantation methods and expand them. These are the main lines
along which fish-farming seem likely to develop; as a long-term aim,
fish-farming must be one of the objects of fisheries research.

Theory

Much of fisheries research in the last thirty years has been concerned
with theory, the development of population dynamics with the use of
fisheries statistics to obtain the best use of fishing. It is a truism that
science develops partly in technique and partly in theory. Each tech-
nical or theoretical advance illuminates a zone for scientific exploration.
Conceptually, the dynamics of fish populations are not very difficult
or complicated. Despite the apparently large quantity of sampled material, there is not enough of it. This is the real difference between
physical statistics and biological statistics; the first deal with adequate
quantities of data, and the second deal with inadequate quantities.

The sampling carried out in the North Sea is inadequate in quantity and in quality, and real theoretical advances will not become possible until quantity data are adequately available. Deterministic models might give way to stochastic ones. The effect of competition and other forms of stock interdependence could be investigated. It is likely that the analysis of tagging experiments will become more precise with Gulland's method (1963), using recaptures per unit of effort. It is also probable that larval mortalities will be properly measured at sea. But the real point is that each theoretical stage has developed rather slowly from the preceding one, and has been delayed by the mean and pinched nature of the data. By this it is meant that the large quantities of data already handled are insufficient to cope with the next stages in theoretical development.

The main use of theory is to point the way to the next stages of biological investigation. A previous chapter has discussed the development of recruitment studies, which really stemmed from a clear understanding of the simple yield equations, but the present requirement in fisheries biology is a more precise analysis of the bases of the parameters of the yield equations. For example, we need a fuller understanding of the growth of fishes, the part played by the reproductive load, the part played by activity, the part played by different qualities of food. Some of these factors have been examined, but not with the self-supporting standards of discipline characteristic of adult sciences. Again new disciplines, like gear research, which should combine those of fish behavior and some parts of hydrodynamics, are being established. There is a requirement to understand and develop gear to catch fish, but we need also to set up a body of knowledge of how the gear generates mortality, how to exploit lacunae in the fishes' behavior, and how this process is modified by the local hydrodynamic situation. In other words, we need to study the catchability coefficients. A quite different and new approach would involve the analysis of gut contents to examine natural mortality, as was done for the birds eating South African pilchards. Extensive sampling of material would be the first stage in a real analysis of the links of dynamic relationship in the sea.

Theoretical advances have spurred many advances in fisheries biology; but other advances have been initiated, particularly in two areas. The first deals with the proper definition of a unit stock. It is a truism that subpopulations have to be separated, and the randomness of mating chances established; fisheries biologists will now have to support these points rigorously. The second area of advance lies in the development of trophic analysis. This consists partly in the making of models of productive cycles in one way or another, and partly in the connection of such methods with those of the yield equations. One major theoretical advance will concern the proper attachment of environmental effects to the yield equations, and presumably the incorporation of yield equations into the trophic models. Then we would really be in a position to understand the great fisheries in the upwelling areas.

However, the most important theoretical problem that needs solution is the dependence of recruitment on parent stock. In Chapter 8 it was noted that within the fishable range of plaice stocks, they are independent. The extension of this argument to other stocks was dogmatic. Indeed, Thompson's (1936) analysis of the Pacific halibut problem states the dogma. Recently, Cushing and Bridger (1966) and Garrod (1967) have published stock vs. recruitment relationships for herring and cod, respectively, which would deny the dogma if the variations in recruitment were not due to environmental causes. But the problem is a difficult one, really depending on our capacity to measure density-dependent mortality of larvae and young fish at sea.

The account of the future of fisheries research is a description of the present development of ideas at the Fisheries Laboratory in Lowestoft. Therefore the outlook is parochial rather than universal, as might be expected, since my room looks out over the southern North Sea. Elsewhere the outlook must be quite different. Here I acknowledge a debt to the people who have worked at Lowestoft, in the past and now.

Reference Matter

Appendix 1
List of Symbols and Their Definitions

English Alphabet

A Area (m², km², or statistical rectangles).

D True density.

E Rate of exploitation $= (F/Z)(1 - e^{-Z})$.

F Fishing mortality coefficient (instantaneous).

G Growth increment.

H Fraction of tagged fish that survive tagging.

J Fraction of total recaptures reported.

K Rate at which length reaches L_∞, the asymptotic length.

L Length.

        L_m = length at maturation.

        L_∞ = asymptotic length.

M Natural mortality coefficient (instantaneous).

N Number of fish.

        N_m = numbers of fish tagged.

        N_r = numbers of fish recaptured.

        N_t = numbers at time t.

     N_0, N_1, N_2, N_λ = abundance or stock density in year 0, year 1, year 2, or year λ.

     $\overline{N}_1, \overline{N}_2$ = average abundance or stock density in year 1 or year 2.

O Average number of eggs per m².

P Stock.

     $\hat{P}$ = estimate of stock size.

     P_e = egg production, or product of stock and fecundity.

     P_m = stock producing maximum recruitment.

     P_n = stock in numbers.

     P_r = replacement size of stock.

     P_s = surplus production.

     P_w = stock in weight.

     $P_{\overline{w}}$ = mean stock in weight.

Q Temperature coefficient of egg development.

R Recruitment.
             R' = number of recruits entering a fishery.
             R_3 = number of recruits as at 3 years of age.
             R_r = recruits from the replacement stock, P_r.
S Constant in a tagging experiment separating type A and type B errors.
T_{max} Maximum recorded age.
W Weight.
             W_∞ = asymptotic weight.
             W_c = weight at first capture.
             W_0, W_1, W_t = weight at time 0, 1, t.
             $\overline{W}_t$ = mean weight at time t.
W' Ratio of stock to replacement stock ($= P/P_r$).
X Other loss coefficient (instantaneous) in a tagging experiment.
Y Catch or yield.
             Y_n = yield in numbers.
             Y_w = yield in weight.
Z Total mortality coefficient (instantaneous).
Z' Increment of total mortality in Russell's equation.

a'' Constant.
a Ratio of replacement stock to maximum stock ($= P_r/P_m$).
c Constant of integration.
d Stock density, or catch per unit of effort.
f Fishing intensity, or fishing effort per unit area.
             $\tilde{f}$ = effective overall fishing intensity.
g Fishing effort, or time spent fishing.
k Number of stations in a statistical rectangle.
l Length.
             l_t = length at time t.
             l_1 = length at the end of the first year's growth in the herring.
m Proportion of larvae in the surface layer.
n Number.
             n_3, n_4, n_5 = numbers of fish per unit of effort, recruiting at ages 3, 4, and 5.
             n_1, n_2 = numbers recaptured in a tagging experiment.
             n_i = number of fish recaptured in area i.
p Concentration of food.
             $\bar{p}$ = mean food density.
q Catchability coefficient ($= q'$).
r Daily ration.
s^2 Variance.
t Time.
             $t_{p'}$ = the age of entry into the fishery.
             t_λ = the age at which a year class is extinguished.
u Percentage of an ingredient, i, of food in the gut.
v Percentage of an ingredient, j, of food in the water.

Greek Alphabet

α Constant expressing the ratio of density-dependent mortality to total mortality in the generation of recruitment.

β   Constant expressing density-independent mortality in the generation of recruitment.

γ   Specific growth rate.

δ, ε   Constants in Gulland's simplified yield equation.

ζ   Index of aggregation.

η   Index of food selection.

θ   Daily ration, as percentage of the maximum ration at zero aggregation.

κ   Feeding coefficient.

λ   Fishable life span between recruitment and extinction.

μ   Coefficient of mortality of recruiting fish as larvae or immatures.

               μ_1 = coefficient of density-independent mortality.

               μ_2 = coefficient of density-dependent mortality.

ν   Deviation in food density.

τ   Equivalent time interval in a tagging experiment.

φ   Translocation rate.

χ   Concentration coefficient.

ψ   Number of tidal cycles per day.

ω   Maximum ration.

Ω_n Summation constant, where $n = +1, -3, +3, -1$.

Appendix 2
Glossary

Age group. The group of fish at a given age. 0 group fish are fish in the first year of life; I group fish are fish in the second year of life; II group fish are fish in the third year of life. A fish born on 1 April remains in the 0 group until 1 April in the subsequent year, after which it is allocated to the I group, II group, etc.

Beam trawl. A small trawl, the mouth of which is held open by a beam between two trawl heads or iron runners.

Cathode ray oscilloscope (CRT). An instrument that displays transient changes of voltage on a phosphorescent screen.

Cran. Originally a measure of volume, equivalent to 37.5 imperial gallons. In weight there are 5.5 crans to a metric ton of herring.

Decca track plotter. An instrument that gives a continuous record, on hyperbolic coordinates, of the ship's position from information given by the "Decca navigator," which is a very accurate navigational instrument, using radio waves.

Demersal. Fish living on, or close to, the seabed.

Discriminatory analysis. A method of discriminating between two populations, using an array of measured characters and minimizing the differences in the whole array.

Distance function. A measure of the "distance" between two populations in terms of the differences used in discriminatory analysis.

Drifter shot. A herring drifter shoots 70–95 nets at dusk and hauls them a few hours later or at the following dawn. The unit operation is termed a "drifter shot."

Drift net. Like a gill net, but the fleet of nets drives with the tide and with the drifter, the fishing boat working the nets.

Elver. A young eel which has metamorphosed and which is usually found in estuaries or on its way up rivers.

Gill net. A curtain of netting suspended from the surface by floats. Single nets are linked into fleets of nets. Fish swim into them in darkness and are caught by their gill covers.

Grab. A spring-loaded double jaw which closes as it is dropped onto the bottom, enclosing a fixed area of soil on the seabed.

Heincke's law. "The size and age of the plaice in a definite part of the North Sea are inversely proportional to the density of their occurrence, but directly proportional to the distance of the locality from the coast and to its depth."

Hensen net. A vertically hauled plankton net with a restricting cone at the mouth of 70 cm in diameter; the mesh size is 60 meshes to the linear inch. The net was designed by Victor Hensen of Kiel toward the end of the nineteenth century.

Hjort maturity stage I. A virgin fish with no gonad growing in the body cavity.

Homing. The return of fish to their native spawning grounds.

Isopleth. Contour.

Log normal. Where the logarithms of a set of variate value are distributed according to a normal curve. It is useful in biological material because the effects of many biological processes, like reproduction, appear in numbers as geometric series.

Midwater. Any part of the water column between the surface and the seabed. Fish living at the surface or on the seabed do not live in midwater.

Migration. The movements of fish from feeding ground to spawning ground and back again, from nursery ground to feeding ground, and from spawning ground to nursery ground.

Natural mortality. The loss in numbers in a year class from one age group to the subsequent one, due to natural death.

Ogive. A cumulative percentage frequency distribution.

Orientation. The choice of a bearing as expressed in the direction of an animal's movement.

Otolith. Earstone, used by fish for its sense of balance. There is one in each plane of the semicircular canals on each side of the head, making six in all. Fishery biologists use the biggest ones to determine the age of fishes.

Otter trawl. A large triangular bag of netting dragged along the seabed. The mouth is spread apart by two boards, one on each towing bridle.

Pair trawler. One of a pair of boats towing a trawl on or near the bottom or in the midwater.

Petersen's young-fish trawl. A small trawl made of shrimp netting, or of finer mesh, towed on a single bridle from which warps to spreading boards diverge and attach to the wings.

Pound net. A net on shore in which fish are impounded. They are also called set nets or fixed engines.

Purse seine. A curtain of net shot at the surface in the form of a circle, an encircling net. It is closed below by ropes passing through purse rings, and this action is called pursing.

Rayleigh's law. Sound is scattered from objects smaller than one-quarter wavelength in diameter, inversely as the fourth power of the wavelength.

Recruitment. The entrance of young fish of a year class into a fishery. The young fish recruit to a fishery over a period, sometimes less than a year and sometimes for one or more years.

Redd. A gravel bed in a river in which salmon lay their eggs.

Smolt. An adolescent salmon which has metamorphosed and which is found on its way downstream toward the sea.

Sonar. An apparatus that uses sound waves to detect objects underwater by measuring or classifying the echoes received from them. An echo sounder is a sonar that transmits vertically. In practice, a sonar is an apparatus other than an echo sounder, i.e., a sonar transmits horizontally.

Soxhlet apparatus. An apparatus for estimating fat content.

Spent herring. A herring that has just spawned, a "shotten" herring.

Sprat. A small herring-like fish living in northern coastal waters (*Clupea sprattus* Linnaeus).

Statistical rectangle. The ocean is divided into rectangles with small sides, e.g., 30 miles, and catches are internationally classified by rectangles.

Steady state. A population in a steady state may fluctuate about a mean but does not increase or decline in a systematic way with time.

Swirl. A gyre on a small scale; it may or may not be temporary.

Target strength. The ratio of received signal to transmitted signal from an object as at 1 m from the transmitter. Although it can be expressed in any units, it is convenient to express target strength in db reference 1 μbar.

Total mortality. The loss in numbers in a year class from one age group to the subsequent one, due to all causes, including sometimes those other than death.

Year brood. Equivalent to year class.

Year class. A brood of fish born in a given year. After the brood recruits to the fishery it reappears year after year until it is extinguished.

Zone electrophoresis. A method of separating proteins (e.g., in blood sera) by their differential migration in an electric field.

References

Ahlstrom, E. H. 1966. Distribution and abundance of sardine and anchovy larvae in the California current region off California and Baja California, 1951–64: A summary. U.S. Fish and Wildlife Serv., Spec. Sci. Rep. 534. 71 p.

Allen, K. R. 1953. A method for computing the optimum size limit for a fishery. Nature, 172(4370):210.

Alward, G. L. 1932. The sea fisheries of Great Britain and Ireland: A record of the development of the fishing industry and its world-wide ramifications. A. Gait, Grimsby. 549 p.

Ancellin, J. 1956. Le hareng du sud de la Mer du Nord et de la Manche orientale —observations de 1945 à 1954. Sci. et Pêche, 21:1–5.

———, and C. Nédelèc. 1959. Marquage de harengs en Mer du Nord et en Manche orientale (Campagne du "Président Théodore Tissier," Novembre 1957). Rev. Trav. Inst. Pêches Marit., 23:177–201.

Bailey, N. T. J. 1951. On estimating the size of mobile populations from recapture data. Biometrika, 38:293–306.

Bainbridge, R. 1960. Speed and stamina in three fish. J. Exp. Biol., 37:129–53.

Baranov, F. I. 1918. On the question of the biological basis of fisheries. Nauchnyi issledovatelskii ikhtiologicheskii Institut Isvestia 1(1):81–128.

Battle, H. I. 1935. Digestion and digestive enzymes in the herring (*Clupea harengus* L.) J. Biol. Board, Can., 1(3):145–57.

Baxter, I. G. 1959. Fecundities of winter-spring and summer-autumn herring spawners. J. Cons. Intern. Explor. Mer, 25(1):73–80.

Bertalanffy, L. von. 1934. Untersuchungen über die Gesetzlichkeit des Wachstums. I. Allgemeine Grundlagen der Theorie; mathematische und physiologische Gesetzlichkeiten des Wachstums bei Wassertieren. Arch. Entwicklungsmech., 131:613–52.

Bertelsen, E., and K. Popp Madsen. 1953–57. Young herring from the Bløden ground area. Ann. Biol., Cons. Intern. Explor. Mer, 9(1953):179–80; 10(1954):155–56; 12(1957):197–98.

Beverton, R. J. H. 1962. Long-term dynamics of certain North Sea fish populations, p. 242–64. *In* E. D. Le Cren and M. W. Holdgate [ed.], The exploitation of natural animal populations. Blackwell, London. 399 p.

———. 1963. Maturation growth, and mortality of clupeid and engraulid stocks in relation to fishing. Rapp. Procès-Verb. Cons. Intern. Explor. Mer, 154:44–67.

————, and S. J. Holt. 1957. On the dynamics of exploited fish populations. H. M. Stationery Off., London, Fish. Invest., Ser. 2, Vol. 19. 533 p.

————, and ————. 1959. A review of the lifespans and mortality rates of fish in nature and the relation to growth and other physiological characteristics, p. 142–77. *In* Ciba Foundation, Colloquia in ageing. V. The lifespan of animals. Churchill, London.

————, and A. J. Lee. 1964. The influence of hydrographic and other factors on the distribution of cod on the Spitzbergen shelf. Intern. Comm. N.W. Atlantic Fish., Environmental Symp., Spec. Pub. No. 6:225–46.

Bidder, G. P. 1925. The mortality of plaice. Nature, 115(2892):495–96.

Blaxter, J. H. S., and W. Dickson. 1959. Observations on the swimming speeds of fish. J. Cons. Intern. Explor. Mer, 24:472–79.

Bodenheimer, F. S. 1938. Problems of animal ecology. Oxford Univ. Press, London. 183 p.

Böhnecke, G. 1922. Salzegehalt und Strömungen der Nordsee. Veröffentlich. Inst. Meeresk. A. Geogr. Naturwiss. Reihe, No. 10:1–34.

Bolster, G. C. 1955. English tagging experiments. Rapp. Procès-Verb. Cons. Intern. Explor. Mer, 140(2):11–14.

Bostrøm, O. 1955. "Peder Ronnestad" Ekkolodding og meldetjeneste av Skreiforekomstene i Lofoten i tiden 1 March–2 Apr. 1955: Praktiske fiskeforsøk 1954 og 1955. Arsberet. Vedkomm. Norges Fisk., 9:66–70.

Bridger, J. P. 1960. On the relationship between stock, larvae and recruits in the "Downs" herring. Cons. Intern. Explor. Mer, Herring Comm., Paper No. 159. 9 p. Mimeograph.

Brody, S. 1945. Bioenergetics and growth, with special reference to the efficiency complex in domestic animals. Reinhold Publ. Corp., New York. 1025 p.

Brown, M. E. 1946a. The growth of brown trout (*Salmo trutta* Linn.). II. The growth of two-year-old trout at a constant temperature of 11.5° C. J. Exp. Biol., 22:130–44.

————. 1946b. The growth of brown trout (*Salmo trutta* Linn.). III. The effect of temperature on the growth of two-year-old trout. J. Exp. Biol., 22:145–55.

Bückmann, A. 1942. Die Untersuchungen der Biologischen Anstalt über die Ökologie der Heringsbrut in der südlichen Nordsee. Helgoland Wiss. Meeresunters., 3:1–57.

Bull, H. O. 1936. Studies on conditioned responses in fishes. VII. Temperature perception in teleosts. J. Mar. Biol. Ass., U.K., N.S., 21:1–27.

Burd, A. C., and J. Bracken. 1965. Studies on the Dunmore herring stock. I. A population assessment. J. Cons. Intern. Explor. Mer, 29(3):277–301.

————, and D. H. Cushing. 1962. I. Growth and recruitment in the herring of the southern North Sea. II. Recruitment to the North Sea herring stocks. H. M. Stationery Off., London, Fish. Invest., Ser. 2, Vol. 23(5). 71 p.

Carlisle, D. B., and E. J. Denton. 1959. On the metamorphosis of the visual pigments of *Anguilla anguilla* (L.). J. Mar. Biol. Ass., U.K., N.S., 38:97–102.

Clark, F. N., and J. C. Marr. 1956. Population dynamics of the Pacific sardine. Calif. Coop. Ocean. Fish. Invest., Prog. Rep., 1 July 1953 to 31 March 1955, p. 11–48.

Clarke, G. L. 1936. The depth at which fish can see. Ecology, 17:452–56.

Colebrook, J. M. 1963. Continuous plankton records: Annual variations in the abundance of *Calanus finmarchicus* 1948–1959. Bull. Mar. Ecol., 6(1):17–30.

Corlett, J. 1958. Distribution of larval cod in the western Barents Sea, p. 281–88. *In* Some problems for biological fishery survey and techniques for their solution. Intern. Comm. N.W. Atlantic Fish., Spec. Pub. No. 1.

Cushing, D. H. 1952. Echo-surveys of fish. J. Cons. Intern. Explor. Mer, 18:45–60.

———. 1957. The number of pilchards in the Channel. H. M. Stationery Off., London, Fish. Invest., Ser. 2, Vol. 21(5). 27 p.

———. 1959a. On the effect of fishing on the herring of the southern North Sea. J. Cons. Intern. Explor. Mer, 24(2):283–307.

———. 1959b. The seasonal variation in oceanic production as a problem in population dynamics. J. Cons. Intern. Explor. Mer, 24(3):455–64.

———. 1960. The East Anglian fishery in 1959. World Fishing, 9(8):51–58.

———. 1961. On the failure of the Plymouth herring fishery. J. Mar. Biol. Ass., U.K., N.S., 41(3):799–816.

———. 1964a. The work of grazing in the sea, p. 207–25. *In* D. J. Crisp [ed.], Grazing in terrestrial and marine environments. Blackwell, London.

———. 1964b. The counting of fish with an echo sounder. Rapp. Procès-Verb. Cons. Intern. Explor. Mer, 155:190–95.

———, and J. P. Bridger. 1966. The stock of herring in the North Sea and changes due to fishing. H. M. Stationery Off., London, Fish. Invest., Ser. 2, Vol. 25(1). 123 p.

———, and A. C. Burd. 1957. On the herring of the southern North Sea. H. M. Stationery Off., London, Fish. Invest., Ser. 2, Vol. 20(11). 31 p.

———, F. R. Harden Jones, R. B. Mitson, G. H. Ellis, and G. Pearce. 1963. Measurements of the target strength of fish. J. Brit. Inst. Electr. and Radio Eng., 25(4):299–303.

———, and H. F. Nicholson. 1963. Studies on a *Calanus* patch. IV. Nutrient salts off the north-east coast of England in the spring of 1954. J. Mar. Biol. Ass., U.K., N.S., 43(2):373–86.

Cushing, J. E. 1956. Observations on serology of tuna. U.S. Fish and Wildlife Serv., Spec. Sci. Rep.—Fish., No. 183. 14 p.

Dahl, K. 1907. The scales of the herring as a means of determining age, growth and migration. Rep. Norweg. Fish. Mar. Invest., 2(6):1–36.

Dannevig, E. H. 1956. Cod populations identified by a chemical method. Fiskeridir. Skr. Ser. Havundersøk., 11 (6). 13 p.

Dannevig, G. 1954. The feeding grounds of the Lofoten cod. Rapp. Procès-Verb. Cons. Intern. Explor. Mer, 136:87–102.

Davies, D. H. 1957. The biology of the South African pilchard. Dep. Comm. Ind., Div. Fish., Union South Africa, Invest. Rep., No. 32:1–10.

———. 1958. The South African pilchard (*Sardinops ocellata*): The predation of sea birds in the commercial fishery. Dep. Comm. Ind., Div. Fish., Union South Africa, Invest. Rep., No. 31:1–15.

Devold, F. 1952. A contribution to the study of the migrations of the Atlanto-Scandian herring. Rapp. Procès-Verb. Cons. Intern. Explor. Mer, 131:103–7.

———. 1963. The life history of the Atlanto-Scandian herring. Rapp. Procès-Verb. Cons. Intern. Explor. Mer, 154:98–108.

Dickie, L. M. 1963. Estimation of mortality rates of Gulf of St. Lawrence cod from results of a tagging experiment. Intern. Comm. N.W. Atlantic Fish., N. Atlantic Fish Marking Symp., Spec. Pub. No. 4:71–80.

Ege, V. 1939. A revision of the genus *Anguilla* Shaw, a systematic, phylogenetic and geographical study. Dana Rep., 3(16):1–256.

Ehrenbaum, E., and H. Marukawa. 1913. Über Altersbestimmung und Wachstum beim Aal. Z. Fisch. Hilfswissen-schaft., 14:89–127.

English, T. S. 1964. A theoretical model for estimating the abundance of planktonic fish eggs. Rapp. Procès-Verb. Cons. Intern. Explor. Mer, 155:174–82.

Farris, D. A. 1960. The effect of three different types of growth curves on estimates of larval fish survival. J. Cons. Intern. Explor. Mer, 25(3):294–306.

Fisher, R. A. 1936. The use of multiple measurements in taxonomic problems. Ann. Eug., London, 7:178–88.

Foerster, R. E. 1936. The return from the sea of sockeye salmon (*Oncorhynchus nerka*) with special reference to percentage survival, sex proportions and progress of migration. J. Biol. Board, Can., 3:26–42.

Fridriksson, A. 1934. On the calculation of age-distribution within a stock of cod by means of relatively few age-determinations as a key to measurements on a large scale. Rapp. Procès-Verb. Cons. Intern. Explor. Mer, 86:1–5.

———, and O. Aasen. 1950. The Norwegian-Icelandic herring tagging experiments. Rep. No. 1. Fiskeridir. Skr. Ser. Havundersøk., 9(11):1–43.

Fukuda, Y. 1962. On the stocks of halibut and their fisheries in the Northeast Pacific. Intern. N. Pacific Fish Comm., Bull. No. 7:39–50.

Fukuhara, F. M. 1955. Japanese high seas mothership type drift gill net salmon fishery, 1954. Comm. Fish. Rev., 17(3):1–12.

———, S. Murai, J.-J. Lalanne, and A. Sribhibhadh. 1962. Continental origin of red salmon as determined from morphological characters. Intern. N. Pacific Fish Comm., Bull. No. 8:15–109.

Garrod, D. J. 1967. Population dynamics of the Arcto-Norwegian cod. J. Fish. Res. Board, Can., 24(1):145–90.

Gilbert, C. H. 1914. Contributions to the life history of the sockeye salmon. No. 1. Rep. Comm. Fish., B.C. [1913], p. 53–78.

———. Contributions to the life history of the sockeye salmon. No. 2. Rep. Comm. Fish., B.C. [1914], p. 45–75.

Gilis, C. 1957. Evolution dans le temps et dans l'espace de la composition des concentrations de harengs exploitées par les pêcheurs belges dans la Mer du Nord au cours de la période 1951–1955. Rapp. Procès-Verb. Cons. Intern. Explor. Mer, 143(1):34–42.

Graham, M. 1935. Modern theory of exploiting a fishery, and application to North Sea trawling. J. Cons. Intern. Explor. Mer, 10(2):264–74.

———. 1958. Fish population assessment by inspection, p. 67–68. *In* Some problems for biological fishery survey and techniques for their solution. Intern. Comm. N.W. Atlantic Fish., Spec. Pub. No. 1.

Grassi, G. B. 1896. The reproduction and metamorphosis of the common eel (Anguilla vulgaris). Quart. J. Microscop. Sci., 39:371–85.

Great Britain. Ministry of Agriculture, Fisheries, and Food, U.K. 1885–1965. Sea fisheries statistical tables. H. M. Stationery Off., London. 80 vol.

———. Ministry of Agriculture, Fisheries, and Food, and Department of Agriculture and Fisheries, Scotland. 1962. Fish stock record, 1961. Mar. Lab., Aberdeen, and Fish. Lab., Lowestoft. 52 p.

Gulland, J. A. 1955a. Estimation of growth and mortality in commercially exploited fish populations. H. M. Stationery Off., London, Fish. Invest., Ser. 2, Vol. 18(9). 46 p.

———. 1955b. On the estimation of population parameters from marked members. Biometrika, 42:269–70.

REFERENCES

————. 1956. On the fishing effort in the English demersal fisheries. H. M. Stationery Off., London, Fish. Invest., Ser. 2, Vol. 20(5). 41 p.

————. 1961. Fishing and the stocks of fish at Iceland. H. M. Stationery Off., London, Fish. Invest., Ser. 2, Vol. 23(4). 52 p.

————. 1963. The estimation of fishing mortality from tagging experiments. Intern. Comm. N.W. Atlantic Fish., N. Atlantic Fish Marking Symp., Spec. Pub. No. 4:218–27.

————. 1964. Manual of methods of fish population analysis. F.A.O. Fish. Tech. Paper No. 40. 61 p.

————. 1966. North Sea plaice stocks. Min. Agr., Fish., Food, London, Lab. Leaflet No. 11. 18 p.

————, and G. R. Williamson. 1962. Transatlantic journey of a tagged cod. Nature, 195(4844):921.

Hardy, A. C., G. T. D. Henderson, C. E. Lucas, and J. H. Fraser. 1936. The ecological relations between the herring and the plankton investigated with the plankton indicator. J. Mar. Biol. Ass., U.K., N.S., 21:147–304.

Hart, T. J., and R. I. Currie. 1960. The Benguela current. Discovery Reports, Vol. 31:1–297.

Hasler, A. D. 1954. Odour perception and orientation in fishes. J. Fish. Res. Board, Can., 11(2):107–29.

————, and H. O. Schwassmann. 1960. Sun orientation of fish at different latitudes. Cold Spring Harbor Symp. Quant. Biol., Biological Clocks, 25:429–41.

Haslett, R. W. G. 1962. Determination of the acoustic back scattering patterns and cross sections of fish. Brit. J. Appl. Phys., 13:349–60.

Heincke, F. 1913. Untersuchungen über die Scholle. Generalbericht. I. Schollenfischerei und Schonmassregeln. Vorläufige kurze Übersicht über die wichtigsten Ergebnisse des Berichts. Rapp. Procès-Verb. Cons. Intern. Explor. Mer, 16:1–70.

Hickling, C. F. 1931. The structure of the otolith of the hake. Quart. J. Microscop. Sci., 74:547–61.

Hildemann, W. H. 1956. Goldfish erythrocyte antigens and serology. Science, 124:315–16.

Hjort, J. 1910. Report on herring investigations until January 1910. Publ. Circ. Cons. Intern. Explor. Mer, 53:1–174.

————. 1914. Fluctuations in the great fisheries of northern Europe viewed in the light of biological research. Rapp. Procès-Verb. Cons. Intern. Explor. Mer, 20:1–228.

————. 1926. Fluctuations in the year classes of important food fishes. J. Cons. Intern. Explor. Mer, 1:1–38.

Hodgson, W. C. 1925. Investigations into the age, length and maturity of the herring of the southern North Sea. II. The composition of the catches in 1922–1924. H.M. Stationery Off., London, Fish. Invest., Ser. 2, Vol. 8(5). 48 p.

————. 1957. The herring and its fishery. Routledge and Kegan Paul, London. 197 p.

Höglund, H. 1955. Swedish herring tagging experiments 1949–1953. Rapp. Procès-Verb. Cons. Intern. Explor. Mer, 140(2):19–29.

Hubbs, C. L. 1921. An ecological study of the life history of the fresh-water atherine fish Labidesthes sicculus. Ecology, 2:262–76.

Hylen, A., L. Midttun, and G. Saetersdal. 1961. Torskeundersøkelsene i Lofoten og i Barentshavet 1960. Fisken og Havet., No. 2:1–14.

International Commission on Whaling. 1964. Fourteenth report of the commission. Intern. Whaling Comm., London. 122 p.

Iselin, C. O. 1936. A study of the circulation of the western North Atlantic. Papers Phys. Oceanogr., 4(4):1–97.

Ivlev, V. S. 1961. The experimental ecology of the feeding of fishes. Yale Univ. Press, New Haven. 302 p.

Johnson, J. H. 1960. Sonic tracking of adult salmon at Bonneville Dam, 1957. U.S. Fish and Wildlife Serv., Fish. Bull., 60(176):471–85.

Jones, F. R. Harden. 1957a. Movements of herring shoals in relation to the tidal current. J. Cons. Intern. Explor. Mer, 22(3):322–28.

————. 1957b. Rotation experiments with blind goldfish. J. Exp. Biol., 34(2): 259–75.

————. 1960. Reactions of fish to stimuli. Proc. Indo-Pac. Fish. Counc. 8th Sess., 3:18–28.

————. 1963. The reaction of fish to moving backgrounds. J. Exp. Biol., 40(3): 437–46.

————. In press. The migration of fish. Arnold, London.

————, and B. S. McCartney. 1962. The use of electronic sector-scanning sonar for following the movements of fish shoals: Sea trials on R.R.S. "Discovery II." J. Cons. Intern. Explor. Mer, 27(2):141–49.

————, and G. Pearce. 1958. Acoustic reflexion experiments with perch (*Perca fluviatilis* Linn.) to determine the proportion of the echo returned by the swim bladder. J. Exp. Biol., 35:437–50.

Jones, J. W. 1959. The salmon. Collins, London. 192 p.

Jordan, R., and A. C. de Vildoso. 1965. La anchoveta (*Engraulis ringens J.*). Conocimiento actual sobre su biologia, ecologia y pesqueria. Inst. Mar Peru, Informe 6:1–52.

King, J. E., and T. S. Hida. 1957. Zooplankton abundance in the central Pacific. II. U.S. Fish and Wildlife Serv., Fish. Bull., 57(118):365–95.

Krefft, G. 1954. Untersuchungen zur Rassenfrage beim Heringe. Mitt. Inst. Seefischerei, Hamburg, 6:12–33.

Lea, E. 1929. The herring's scale as a certificate of origin. Its applicability to race investigations. Rapp. Procès-Verb. Cons. Intern. Explor. Mer, 54:21–34.

————. 1930. Mortality in the tribe of Norwegian herring. Rapp. Procès-Verb. Cons. Intern. Explor. Mer, 65:100–117.

Lee, A. J. 1952. The influence of hydrography on the Bear Island cod fishery. Rapp. Procès-Verb. Cons. Intern. Explor. Mer, 131:74–102.

Le Gall, J. 1935. Le hareng, *Clupea harengus*, Linné. I. Les populations de l'Atlantique Nord Est. Ann. Inst. Océanogr., 15:1–215.

Legendre, R. 1934. La faune pélagique de l'Atlantique au large du Golfe de Gascogne recueillie dans des estomacs de germons. I. Poissons. Ann. Inst. Océanogr., 14(6):247–418.

Lundbeck, J. 1954. German market investigations on cod, mainly in the north-eastern area. Rapp. Procès-Verb. Cons. Intern. Explor. Mer, 136:33–39.

McAllister, C. D., T. R. Parsons, and J. D. H. Strickland. 1960. Primary productivity and fertility at station "P" in the north-east Pacific Ocean. J. Cons. Intern. Explor. Mer, 25(3):240–59.

Margolis, L., F. C. Cleaver, Y. Fukuda, and H. Godfrey. 1966. Salmon of the North Pacific. VI. Sockeye salmon in offshore waters. Intern. N. Pacific Fish. Comm., Bull. No. 20:1–68.

Marr, J. C. 1951. On the use of the terms *abundance, availability* and *apparent abundance* in fishery biology. Copeia, 2:163–69.

———. 1956. The "critical period" in the early life history of marine fishes. J. Cons. Intern. Explor. Mer, 21(2):160–70.

———. 1960. The causes of major variations in the catch of the Pacific sardine *Sardinops caerulea* (Girard). World Sci. Meet. Biol. Sardines and Related Species, Proc., 3:667–791.

Maslov, N. A. 1944. Bottom fishes of the Barents Sea. Knipovich Inst., Murmansk, Trans., 8:3–186.

Medawar, P. B., ed. 1945. Size, shape and age: Essays on growth and form presented to D'Arcy Wentworth Thompson. Clarendon Press, Oxford. 408 p.

Meek, A. 1916. The migrations of fish. Arnold, London. 427 p.

Midttun, L., and L. Hoff. 1962. Measurements of the reflection of sound by fish. Fiskeridir. Skr. Ser. Havundersøk., 13(3). 18 p.

Motoda, S., and Y. Hirano. 1963. Review of Japanese herring investigations. Rapp. Procès-Verb. Cons. Intern. Explor. Mer, 154:249–262.

Murphy, G. I. 1966. Population biology of the Pacific sardine (*Sardinops caerulea*). Calif. Acad. Sci., Proc., Ser. 4, Vol. 34(1):1–84.

———, and R. S. Shomura. 1955. Longline fishing for deep-swimming tunas in the central Pacific, August–November 1952. U.S. Fish and Wildlife Serv., Spec. Sci. Rep.—Fish., No. 137. 42 p.

Muzinic, R., and B. B. Parrish. 1960. Some observations on the body proportions of North Sea autumn spawning herring. J. Cons. Intern. Explor. Mer, 25(2): 191–203.

Nikolsky, G. V. 1953. On some regularities of fecundity dynamics in fishes, p. 119–206. *In* his The essay of the general problems of ichthyology. Acad. Sci., U.S.S.R., 36.

Otsu, T. 1960. Albacore migration and growth in the north Pacific Ocean as estimated from tag recoveries. Pacific Sci., 14(3):257–66.

Paloheimo, J. E. 1961. Studies on estimation of mortalities. I. Comparison of a method described by Beverton and Holt and a new linear formula. J. Fish. Res. Board, Can., 18(5):645–62.

Parrish, B. B., I. G. Baxter, and M. J. D. Mowat. 1960. An automatic fish egg counter. Nature, 185(4715):777.

———, and R. E. Craig. 1963. The herring of the northwestern North Sea—Post war changes in the stock fished by Scottish drifters. Cons. Intern. Explor. Mer, Herring Symp. [1961], 154:139–58.

Pearcy, W. G. 1962. Ecology of young winter flounder in an estuary. Peabody Mus. Natur. Hist., Yale Univ., New Haven, Conn., Bull. Bingham Oceanogr. Coll., 18:1–78.

Petersen, C. G. J. 1896. The yearly immigration of young plaice into the Limfjord from the German Sea. Rep. Dansk. Biol. Sta. [1895], 6:1–48.

Poulsen, E. M. 1930a. On the fluctuations in the abundance of cod fry in the Kattegat and the Belt Sea and causes of the same. Rapp. Procès-Verb. Cons. Intern. Explor. Mer, 65:26–30.

———. 1930b. Investigations of fluctuations in the cod stock in Danish waters. Rapp. Procès-Verb. Cons. Intern. Explor. Mer, 68:20–23.

Pritchard, A. L. 1938. Transplantation of pink salmon (*Oncorhynchus gorbuscha*) into Masset inlet, British Columbia, in the barren years. J. Biol. Board, Can., 4:141–50.

————. 1939. Homing tendency and age at maturity of pink salmon (*Oncorhynchus gorbuscha*) in British Columbia. J. Fish. Res. Board, Can., 4:233–51.

————. 1948. A discussion of the mortality in pink salmon (*Oncorhynchus gorbuscha*) during their period of marine life. Roy. Soc. Can., Trans., Ser. 3, Vol. 42:125–33.

Probst, R. T., and E. L. Cooper. 1954. Age, growth, and production of the lake sturgeon (*Acipenser fulvescens*) in the Lake Winnebago region, Wisconsin. Am. Fish. Soc., Trans., 84:207–27.

Rao, C. R. 1952. Advanced statistical methods in biometric research. John Wiley and Sons, New York. 390 p.

Richardson, I. D., D. H. Cushing, F. R. Harden Jones, R. J. H. Beverton, and R. W. Blacker. 1959. Echo sounding experiments in the Barents Sea. H. M. Stationery Off., London, Fish. Invest., Ser. 2, Vol. 22(9). 55 p.

Ricker, W. E. 1940. Relation of "catch per unit effort" to abundance and rate of exploitation. J. Fish. Res. Board, Can., 5:43–70.

————. 1945. Abundance, exploitation and mortality of the fishes in two lakes. Invest. Indiana Lakes and Streams, 2(17):345–448.

————. 1948. Methods of estimating vital statistics of fish populations. Bloomington, Indiana Univ. Pub., Sci. Ser., No. 15. 101 p.

————. 1954. Stock and recruitment. J. Fish. Res. Board, Can., 11(5): 559–623.

————. 1958. Handbook of computations for biological statistics of fish populations. Fish. Res. Board, Can., Bull. No. 119. 300 p.

Ridgway, G. J., J. E. Cushing, and G. L. Durall. 1958. Serological differentiation of populations of sockeye salmon, *Oncorhynchus nerka*. U.S. Fish and Wildlife Serv., Spec. Sci. Rep.—Fish., No. 257. 9 p.

Rollefsen, G. 1934. The cod otolith as a guide to race, sexual development and mortality. Rapp. Procès-Verb. Cons. Intern. Explor. Mer, 88(2):1–5.

————. 1953. The selectivity of different fishing gear used in Lofoten. J. Cons. Intern. Explor. Mer, 19(2):191–94.

————. 1954. Observations on the cod and cod fisheries of Lofoten. Rapp. Procès-Verb. Cons. Intern. Explor. Mer, 136:40–47.

————. 1955. The arctic cod. UN Sci. Conf. Conserv. Utiliz. Resources, Proc., Rome, p. 115–17.

Rounsefell, G. A. 1958. Factors causing decline in sockeye salmon of Karluk River, Alaska. U.S. Fish and Wildlife Serv., Fish. Bull. 58(130):83–169.

Russell, E. S. 1931. Some theoretical considerations on the "overfishing" problem. J. Cons. Intern. Explor. Mer, 6(1):3–20.

Saetersdal, G., and A. Hylen. 1959. Skreiundersøkelsene og skreifisket i 1959. Fisken og Havet., No. 1:1–18.

Savage, R. E. 1937. The food of North Sea herring, 1930–1934. H. M. Stationery Off., London, Fish. Invest., Ser. 2, Vol. 15(5). 60 p.

Schaefer, M. B. 1954. Some aspects of the dynamics of populations important to the management of the commercial marine fisheries. Inter-Amer. Trop. Tuna Comm., Bull. 1(2):27–56.

Schmidt, J. 1909. The distribution of the pelagic fry and the spawning regions of the gadoids in the North Atlantic from Iceland to Spain. Rapp. Procès-Verb. Cons. Intern. Explor. Mer, Vol. 10B, Spec. part 4. 158 p.

————. 1914. First report on eel investigations 1913. Rapp. Procès-Verb. Cons. Intern. Explor. Mer, 18:1–30.

————. 1915. Second report on eel investigations, 1915. Rapp. Procès-Verb. Cons. Intern. Explor. Mer, 23:1–24.

—————. 1917. Racial investigations. I. *Zoarces viviparus* L. and local races of the same. Comptes rendus Trav. Lab., Carlsberg, 13(3):279–396.

—————. 1922. The breeding places of the eel. Roy. Soc. London, Phil. Trans., Ser. B, Vol. 211:179–208.

—————. 1930. Racial investigations. X. The Atlantic cod (*Gadus callarias* L.) and local races of the same. Comptes rendus Trav. Lab., Carlsberg, 18(6):1–72.

Scofield, W. L. 1929. Sardine fishing methods at Monterey, California. Calif. Dep. Nat. Res., Div. Fish and Game, Fish. Bull., No. 19. 61 p.

Shelbourne, J. E. 1956. The abnormal development of plaice embryos and larvae in marine aquaria. J. Mar. Biol. Ass., U.K., N.S., 35(1):177–92.

—————. 1963. Marine fish culture in Britain. II. A plaice rearing experiment at Port Erin, Isle of Man, during 1960, in open sea water circulation. J. Cons. Intern. Explor. Mer, 28(1):70–79.

—————, J. D. Riley, and G. T. Thacker. 1963. Marine fish culture in Britain. I. Plaice rearing in closed circulation at Lowestoft, 1957–1960. J. Cons. Intern. Explor. Mer, 28(1):50–69.

Sick, K. 1962. Nye metoder til raceundersogelser af fisk. Skr. Danmarks Fisk. og Havundersøk., 22:13–16.

Silliman, R. P., and F. N. Clark. 1945. Catch per-unit-of-effort in California waters of the sardine (*Sardinops caerulea*) 1932–1942. Calif. Dep. Nat. Res., Div. Fish and Game, Fish. Bull., No. 62. 78 p.

Simpson, A. C. 1959. The spawning of the plaice in the North Sea. H. M. Stationery Off., London, Fish. Invest., Ser. 2, Vol. 22(7). 100 p.

Sindermann, C. J. 1961. Serological techniques in fishery research. 26th N. Amer. Wildlife and Nat. Resources Conf., Trans., p. 298–309.

—————, and D. F. Mairs. 1959. The C blood group system of Atlantic sea herring. Anat. Rec., 134:640.

Steele, J. H. 1961. The environment of a herring fishery. Fisheries, Scotland, Mar. Res. 1961, No. 6. 18 p.

Stommel, H. 1958. The gulf stream: A physical and dynamical description. Cambridge Univ. Press, London. 248 p.

Strasburg, D. W. 1959. An instance of natural mass mortality of larval frigate mackerel in the Hawaiian Islands. J. Cons. Intern. Explor. Mer, 24(2):255–63.

Swallow, J. C., and L. V. Worthington. 1961. An observation of a deep counter current in the western North Atlantic. Deep Sea Res., 8:1–19.

Tait, J. B. 1930. The surface drift in the northern and middle areas of the North Sea and in the Faroe–Shetland Channel. II. Sect. 1. A cartographical analysis of the results of Scottish surface drift bottle experiments commenced in the year 1910. Fisheries, Scotland, Sci. Invest. 1930, No. 4. 56 p.

—————. 1937. The surface water drift in the northern and middle areas of the North Sea and in the Faroe–Shetland Channel. II. Sect. 3. A cartographical analysis of the results of Scottish surface drift bottle experiments of the year 1912; with a discussion on some hydrographical and biological implications of the drift bottle results of 1910, 1911 and 1912, including a statement of a theory of the upper water circulation of the northern and middle North Sea. Fisheries, Scotland, Sci. Invest. 1937, No. 1. 60 p.

Tanaka, S. 1962. On the salmon stocks of the Pacific coast of the United States and Canada (views of the Japanese National Section on the abstention cases of the United States and Canada). Intern. N. Pacific Fish. Comm., Bull. No. 9:69–85.

Tåning, A. V., H. Einarsson, and J. Eggvin. 1955. Records from the month of

June of the Norwegian–Icelandic herring stock in the open ocean. Ann. Biol., Cons. Intern. Explor. Mer, 12:165–67.

Taylor, C. C. 1958. Cod growth and temperature. J. Cons. Intern. Explor. Mer, 23(3):366–70.

Thompson, W. F. 1936. Conservation of the Pacific halibut, an international experiment. Ann. Rep. Smithsonian Inst. 1935, p. 361–82.

Tiews, K. 1963. Synopsis of biological data on bluefin tuna *Thunnus thynnus* (Linnaeus) 1758 (Atlantic and Mediterranean). F.A.O. Fish. Rep. No. 6. F.A.O. World Sci. Meet. Biol. Tunas and Related Species, Proc., Species Synopsis, 12:422–81.

Townsend, C. H. 1935. The distribution of certain whales as shown by logbook records of American whaleships. Zoologica, 19:1–50.

Trout, G. C. 1957. The Bear Island cod: Migration and movements. H. M. Stationery Off., London, Fish. Invest., Ser. 2, Vol. 21(6). 51 p.

Uda, M. 1959. Oceanographic seminars. 2. Watermass boundaries—"Siome": Frontal theory in oceanography. Fish. Res. Board, Can., MS Rep. Ser. (Oceanogr. and Limnol.). 51 p.

Van Campen, W. G. (transl.) 1960. Japanese summer fishery for albacore (*Germo alalunga*). U.S. Fish and Wildlife Serv., Res. Rep., No. 52. 29 p.

Veen, J. F. de. 1961. On the subpopulations of plaice in the southern North Sea. Cons. Intern. Explor. Mer, Near Northern Seas Comm., Paper No. 94. 10 p.

———, and L. K. Boerema. 1959. Distinguishing southern North Sea populations of plaice by means of otolith characteristics. Cons. Intern. Explor. Mer, Near Northern Seas Comm., Paper No. 91. 5 p. Mimeograph.

Walford, L. A. 1946. A new graphic method of describing the growth of animals. Biol. Bull., 90(2):141–47.

Wimpenny, R. S. 1953. The plaice, being the Buckland lectures for 1949. Arnold, London. 144 p.

Winberg, G. G. 1956. Rate of metabolism and food requirements of fishes. Nauch. Trud. Belorusskovo Gos. Univ. i meni. V. I. Lenina, Minsk. 253 p.

Wood, H. 1937. Movements of herring in the northern North Sea. Fisheries, Scotland, Sci. Invest. 1937, No. 3. 49 p.

Woodhead, P. M. J. 1965. Effects of light upon behaviour and distribution of demersal fishes of the North Atlantic. Intern. Comm. N.W. Atlantic Fish., Environmental Symp., Spec. Pub. 6:267–88.

———, and A. D. Woodhead. 1959. The effects of low temperatures on the physiology and distribution of the cod, *Gadus morhua* L., in the Barents Sea. Zool. Soc. London, Proc., 133(2):181–99.

Yamanaka, I. 1960. Comparative study of the population size of Japanese and California sardine. F.A.O. World Sci. Meet. Biol. Sardines and Related Species, Proc., 3:1151–92.

Zijlstra, J. J. 1958. On the herring "races" spawning in the southern North Sea and English Channel (preliminary report). Rapp. Procès-Verb. Cons. Intern. Explor. Mer, 143(2):134–45.

Acknowledgments

Figure 1. M. Graham, 1958. Fish population assessment by inspection, p. 67–68. *In* Some problems for biological fishery survey and techniques for their solution. Intern. Comm. N.W. Atlantic Fish., Spec. Pub. No. 1.

Figures 3 (left and right), 38, 42 (top), 43, 44, 45. R. J. H. Beverton and S. J. Holt, 1957. On the dynamics of exploited fish populations. Fish. Invest., Ser. 2, Vol. 19, 533 p. With the permission of the Controller of Her Britannic Majesty's Stationery Office, London.

Figure 4. D. H. Cushing, 1957. The number of pilchards in the Channel. Fish. Invest., Ser. 2, Vol. 21(5), 27 p. With the permission of the Controller of Her Britannic Majesty's Stationery Office, London.

Figure 5. A. C. Hardy, G. T. D. Henderson, C. E. Lucas, and J. H. Fraser, 1936. The ecological relations between the herring and the plankton investigated with the plankton indicator. J. Mar. Biol. Ass., U.K., N.S., 21:147–304. With the permission of the Cambridge University Press.

Figures 6, 39. J. Ancellin and C. Nédelèc, 1959. Marquage de harengs en Mer du Nord et en Manche orientale (Campagne du "Président Théodore Tissier," Novembre 1957). Rev. Trav. Inst. Pêches Marit., 23:177–201.

Figure 8. W. C. Hodgson, 1957. The herring and its fishery. Routledge and Kegan Paul, Ltd., London. 197 p.

Figure 11. J. C. Corlett, 1958. Distribution of larval cod in the western Barents Sea, p. 281–88. *In* Some problems for biological fishery survey and techniques for their solution. Intern. Comm. N.W. Atlantic Fish., Spec. Pub. No. 1.

Figure 12. J. Schmidt, 1922. The breeding places of the eel. Roy. Soc. London, Phil. Trans., Ser. B, Vol. 211:179–208.

Figures 15, 35. A. C. Simpson, 1959. The spawning of the plaice in the North Sea. Fish. Invest., Ser. 2, Vol. 22(7), 100 p. With the permission of the Controller of Her Britannic Majesty's Stationery Office, London.

Figure 16. J. F. de Veen and L. K. Boerema, 1959. Distinguishing southern North Sea populations of plaice by means of otolith characteristics. Cons. Intern. Explor. Mer, Near Northern Seas Comm., Paper No. 91. 5 p. Mimeograph.

Figures 19, 27, 28, 29, 30, 31, 32, 42 (bottom). D. H. Cushing and J. P. Bridger, 1966. The stock of herring in the North Sea and changes due to fishing. Fish. Invest., Ser. 2, Vol. 25(1), 123 p. With the permission of the Controller of Her Britannic Majesty's Stationery Office, London.

Figure 20. G. Saetersdal and A. Hylen, 1959. Skreiundersøkelsene og skreifisket i 1959. Fisken og Havet., No. 1:1–18.

Figure 21. O. Bostrøm, 1955. "Peder Ronnestad" Ekkolodding og meldetjeneste av Skreiforekomstene i Lofoten i tiden 1 March–2 Apr. 1955: Praktiske fiskeforsøk 1954 og 1955. Arsberet. Vedkomm. Norges Fisk., 9:66–70.

Figure 22. J. Hjort, 1914. Fluctuations in the great fisheries of northern Europe viewed in the light of biological research. Rapp. Procès-Verb. Cons. Intern. Explor. Mer, 20:1–228.

Figure 23. G. Dannevig, 1954. The feeding grounds of the Lofoten cod. Rapp. Procès-Verb. Cons. Intern. Explor. Mer, 136:87–102.

Figures 24, 80. I. D. Richardson, D. H. Cushing, F. R. Harden Jones, R. J. H. Beverton, and R. W. Blacker, 1959. Echo sounding experiments in the Barents Sea. Fish. Invest., Ser. 2, Vol. 22(9), 55 p. With the permission of the Controller of Her Britannic Majesty's Stationery Office, London.

Figure 25. A. Hylen, L. Midttun, and G. Saetersdal, 1961. Torskeundersøkelsene i Lofoten og i Barentshavet 1960. Fisken og Havet., No. 2:1–14.

Figures 26, 57, 59. A. C. Burd and D. H. Cushing, 1962. I. Growth and recruitment in the herring of the southern North Sea. II. Recruitment to the North Sea herring stocks. Fish. Invest., Ser. 2, Vol. 23(5), 71 p. With the permission of the Controller of Her Britannic Majesty's Stationery Office, London.

Figure 33. G. Rollefsen, 1953. The selectivity of different fishing gear used in Lofoten. J. Cons. Intern. Explor. Mer, 19(2):191–94.

Figure 36. S. Tanaka, 1962. On the salmon stocks of the Pacific coast of the United States and Canada (views of the Japanese National Section on the abstention cases of the United States and Canada). Intern. N. Pacific Fish. Comm., Bull. No. 9:69–85.

Figure 37. J. P. Bridger, 1960. On the relationship between stock, larvae and recruits in the "Downs" herring. Cons. Intern. Explor. Mer, Herring Comm., Paper No. 159. 9 p. Mimeograph.

Figure 40. L. M. Dickie, 1963. Estimation of mortality rates of Gulf of St. Lawrence cod from results of a tagging experiment. Intern. Comm. N.W. Atlantic Fish., N. Atlantic Fish Marking Symp., Spec. Pub. No. 4:71–80.

Figure 41. J. A. Gulland, 1963. The estimation of fishing mortality from tagging experiments. Intern. Comm. N.W. Atlantic Fish., N. Atlantic Fish Marking Symp., Spec. Pub. No. 4:218–27.

Figure 46. D. H. Cushing, 1959a. On the effect of fishing on the herring of the southern North Sea. J. Cons. Intern. Explor. Mer, 24(2):283–307.

Figure 47. J. A. Gulland, 1961. Fishing and the stocks of fish at Iceland. Fish. Invest., Ser. 2, Vol. 23(4), 52 p. With the permission of the Controller of Her Britannic Majesty's Stationery Office, London.

Figure 48. C. C. Taylor, 1958. Cod growth and temperature. J. Cons. Intern. Explor. Mer, 23(3):366–70.

Figures 49, 50. R. J. H. Beverton and S. J. Holt, 1959. A review of the lifespans and mortality rates of fish in nature and the relation to growth and other physiological characteristics, p. 142–77. *In* Ciba Foundation, Colloquia in ageing. V. The lifespan of animals. J. & A. Churchill Ltd., London.

Figures 51, 52, 53. V. S. Ivlev, 1961. The experimental ecology of the feeding of fishes. Yale Univ. Press, New Haven. 302 p.

Figures 54, 55. D. H. Cushing, 1964a. The work of grazing in the sea, p. 207–25. *In* D. J. Crisp [ed.], Grazing in terrestrial and marine environments. Blackwell, London.

Figure 56. D. H. Cushing, 1960. The East Anglian fishery in 1959. World Fishing, 9(8):51–58.

Figure 58. D. H. Cushing and A. C. Burd, 1957. On the herring of the southern North Sea. Fish. Invest., Ser. 2, Vol. 20(11), 31 p. With the permission of the Controller of Her Britannic Majesty's Stationery Office, London.

Figure 60. J. C. Marr, 1960. The causes of major variations in the catch of the Pacific sardine *Sardinops caerulea* (Girard). World Sci. Meet. Biol. Sardines and Related Species, Proc., 3:667–791. With the permission of the Food and Agriculture Organization of the United Nations, Rome.

Figure 61(A). I. Yamanaka, 1960. Comparative study of the population size of Japanese and California sardine. World Sci. Meet. Biol. Sardines and Related Species, Proc., 3:1151–92. With the permission of the Food and Agriculture Organization of the United Nations, Rome.

Figure 61 (B). S. Motoda and Y. Hirano, 1963. Review of Japanese herring investigations. Rapp. Procès-Verb. Cons. Intern. Explor. Mer, 154:249–262.

Figure 61 (C). F. Devold, 1963. The life history of the Atlanto–Scandian herring. Rapp. Procès-Verb. Cons. Intern. Explor. Mer, 154:98–108.

Figures 62, 63. R. J. H. Beverton, 1962. Long-term dynamics of certain North Sea fish populations, p. 242–64. *In* E. D. Le Cren and M. W. Holdgate [ed.], The exploitation of natural animal populations. Blackwell, London. 399 p.

Figure 64. J. C. Marr, 1956. The "critical period" in the early life history of marine fishes. J. Cons. Intern. Explor. Mer, 21(2):160–70.

Figure 65. W. G. Pearcy, 1962. Ecology of young winter flounder in an estuary. Peabody Mus. Natur. Hist., Yale Univ., New Haven, Conn. Bull. Bingham Oceanogr. Coll., 18:1–78.

Figures 67, 68. W. E. Ricker, 1958. Handbook of computations for biological statistics of fish populations. Fish. Res. Board, Can., Bull. No. 119. 300 p.

Figure 69. International Commission on Whaling, 1964. Fourteenth report of the commission. Intern. Whaling Comm., London, 122 p.

Figures 71, 72. A. J. Lee, 1952. The influence of hydrography on the Bear Island cod fishery. Rapp. Procès-Verb. Cons. Intern. Explor. Mer, 131:74–102.

Figure 74. A. V. Tåning, H. Einarsson, and J. Eggvin, 1955. Records from the month of June of the Norwegian–Icelandic herring stock in the open ocean. Ann. Biol., Cons. Intern. Explor. Mer, 12:165–67.

Figure 75. C. H. Townsend, 1935. The distribution of certain whales as shown by logbook records of American whaleships. Zoologica, 19:1–50.

Figure 76. T. J. Hart and R. I. Currie, 1960. The Benguela current. Discovery Reports, Vol. 31:1–297. With the permission of the National Institute of Oceanography.

Figure 77. D. H. Davies, 1958. The South African pilchard (*Sardinops ocellata*): The predation of sea birds in the commercial fishery. Dep. Comm. Ind., Div. Fish., Union South Africa, Invest. Rep., No. 31:1–15.

Figure 78. F. R. Harden Jones, 1957a. Movements of herring shoals in relation to the tidal current. J. Cons. Intern. Explor. Mer, 22(3):322–28.

Figure 79. F. R. Harden Jones and B. S. McCartney, 1962. The use of electronic sector-scanning sonar for following the movements of fish shoals: Sea trials on R.R.S. "Discovery II." J. Cons. Intern. Explor. Mer, 27(2):141–49.

Figure 82. J. E. Shelbourne, J. D. Riley, and G. T. Thacker, 1963. Marine fish culture in Britain. I. Plaice rearing in closed circulation at Lowestoft, 1957–1960. J. Cons. Intern. Explor. Mer, 28(1):50–69.

Index